Q

is for

QUANTUM

Terry Rudolph

For permission requests, please contact: terry@qisforquantum.org

ISBN: 978-0-9990635-0-7

www.qisforquantum.org

Cover design by Chris Van Diepen, createwithbodhi.com

Interior design by booknook.biz

For Xavier, Aby, Lydia, Jesse and Caleb

& Marta!

Hope you enjoy learning
some new quantum tricks ☺

Terry

TABLE OF CONTENTS

Preface

This book has been written for my 15-year-old self. Well, there is plenty of advice I would give my 15-year-old self that you don't want to hear, and there are very many things I was very interested in at 15 that are not covered here. But one thing I was interested in at that age was science, and I distinctly recall being frustrated by the lack of concrete explanations within "pop-sci" accounts of modern physics. The exciting descriptions I found in them were ultimately hollow. They were vague on details and they came loaded with jargon, questionable analogies, and somewhat mysterious pontifications about the nature of physical reality. Implicitly justifying the lack of explanation were historical anecdotes about how these discoveries confused all the famous physicists who made them as well.

As someone who wanted to tackle these mysteries (perhaps solving them before I left high school!) the situation was frustrating. Having failed to solve the mysteries by 17, I was forced to go and waste years studying physics at university. The failures kept piling up, and I have ended up a professional physicist who is still both confused and amazed by our physical laws.

A fairly recent mathematical breakthrough (not by me) suggested a very different method of presenting some of the most interesting and weird phenomena of modern physics.

Through my talks to teenagers I have found it is possible for students who know only arithmetic to quantitatively—not just qualitatively—understand the most important features of many of our deepest confusions about what is going on in the natural world. In fact, my nine-year-old nephew understood why there is a genuine mystery about what could "really be" happening inside the PETE boxes introduced in Part I and a few days later asked me whether I have solved it yet. Perhaps he wanted to solve it himself before leaving primary school.

I eventually decided to write down the method I use, and here it is. Of course it is very much easier explaining this kind of thing in the back-and-forth dialogue of a classroom. It would be awesome if high-school teachers got interested in this approach and felt comfortable enough to explain these wonderful things to their students. I welcome feedback about what other resources I could provide to facilitate this.

Introduction

This is a book about physical phenomena I find deeply mysterious; about how we plan to harness them in amazing new technologies despite not really understanding them; and about where we stand in our attempts to obtain such an understanding.

We use mathematics to help us describe things going on in the physical world around us. This is not only because quantitative statements (which are precise and technical, such as: "If you fall out of a tree twice as high it will take 1.4142... times as long to hit the ground, regardless of the tree height or what size planet you are on") are more useful than qualitative ones (which are fuzzy and vague, such as: "Well, duh, it'll take longer becoz the tree is higher, which planet are you on?"). Rather, to a physicist, the math is an inextricable part of our understanding. Many times we have successfully predicted the existence of new physical objects and new physical phenomena based on the math alone.

The mathematical equations of physics—the "physical laws"—typically provide us with precise and beautifully intricate rules by which we understand how physical things we either observe directly, or otherwise believe exist, connect to each other. This lets us build a story, a narrative, about what is "really" going on. It does sometimes happen, however, that

1

we are uncertain about the exact connection between the useful math and the physical world. For example, prior to the direct observation of atoms, some doubted their existence for this sort of reason.

Modern physics is in an odd situation. Some of our most important physical laws lead to a very strange (many would say completely nonsensical) narrative about what is "actually" going on when we view the mathematical objects in the theory as corresponding to something physically real.

More precisely then, this is a book about the tension between the abstract math, the observed physics, and the inferred story. Along the way the goal is to elucidate both strengths and limitations of some of the very cool new technologies we are currently building based on these incompletely understood laws.

Unfortunately, not everyone is good at mathematics, and most have little, if any, training in physics. So to tell the remarkable story of this ongoing intellectual adventure and the controversy around it, I (and many others) typically have resorted to qualitative expositions. These are very, very limited, and appreciating them alone simply will not let you make a meaningful contribution to the discussion, despite many emails I receive from crackpots suggesting the contrary. It is like only having van Gogh's "Starry Night" described in words to you, by someone who has only seen a black and white photograph. One that a dog chewed.

I recently came to the realization that it is possible to do much better than this. I believe I can help you properly understand most of the mysteries that swirl around our abject failure to take some mathematical equations—which unquestionably describe experiments we can do—and underpin them with a universally accepted physical narrative.

Nominally, the only math required in this book is the arithmetic of positive and negative integers. But in fact the drawings you will see in subsequent pages are mathematics. They are symbols on paper that we manipulate according to fixed rules, which have subtle relationships with each other, and which act as shortcuts for much longer and wordier descriptions. All math is really just this. What I am doing with all these drawings is what theoretical physicists do for a living—play around with numbers and equations and diagrams to try to describe certain things that we observe (or suspect) happen. When we find some that seem to explain the situation consistently, we are delighted if puzzled, and use them to do more complex calculations pertaining to related happenings. As long as the outcomes fit with the observations, we feel somewhat happy with our equations. But ultimately we would like to feel we "really understand" what our mathematics "means" in terms of stuff that actually goes on in the physical world.

I begin in Part I by presenting some simple but amazing experiments we can do, building up the math we use to describe them. From this I will be able to show you how we will soon build new types of computers, ones that think using a logic very differently to ours. We can do this even though we don't have a deep understanding of what is going on inside them at the underlying physical level. In Part II we will tackle the strange phenomena of nonlocality and entanglement; for me these were the gateway drug to physics. In Part III we go on a trip that may make you wonder if physicists are on other kinds of drugs too, as we explore the strong incompatibility between the "physical realism" we simply take for granted, and any sensible narrative about what is actually going on.

I really should spend a few more pages spouting profound-sounding blather, both to set up the story of this book and entice you to buy it. But while you are mentally fresh I'd rather get you to concentrate on some technical things.

Part I: Q-COMPUTING

Black balls or white balls?

Imagine you have a box which has a hole in the top and a hole in the bottom. (I say "imagine," but I want to emphasize from the start that what follows is not an analogy, but rather a description of physical devices which we could, in principle, build. They are constructible according to the laws of physics as we know them today. However, the prohibitive cost and engineering challenges of building them means we do not actually try to do these experiments this way—we use other physical setups which are less easy to describe, but which have identical functionality.)

OK, back to your box with a hole in the top and bottom. You can drop either a black or a white ball into the hole in the top, and as it falls through the color flips. If you drop in a black ball, it comes out the bottom hole white. If you drop in a white ball, it comes out black. You could label this box "flip" or "change," but for various reasons it is traditionally labeled "NOT," since a white ball comes out "not-white," i.e. black, and vice versa.

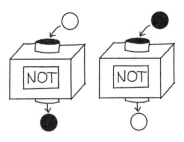

Next imagine you have a different type of box with two holes in the top, and two in the bottom. You discover that if you simultaneously drop one ball in each top hole, then the balls which emerge from the bottom have their color swapped with each other:

Looking at the balls coming through the first and fourth boxes one might be unsure that a swap had occurred, but it did—white just swapped for white and black for black. Dropping balls of different colors into the second and third boxes makes this clear. We may wonder then if the box is swapping the balls themselves. To check, we can use a plastic ball on the left and a metal one on the right. We find that the ball entering a hole always drops out from the hole directly below it, only the colors have swapped.

Another two-ball box is the CNOT or "controlled-NOT." This is a box where a NOT happens to one of the balls, the "target" ball, based on whether the other "control" ball is "switched on" by being black. If the control ball is white, nothing happens. In either case, the control ball's color is always unaffected:

A useful three-ball box is the CSWAP or "controlled-SWAP". Here is how it works on all possible input colors of balls:

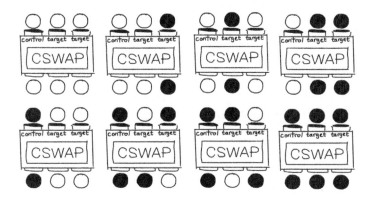

Like the CNOT, nothing happens to any of the three balls when the control ball is white, as you see in the first row of boxes. When it is black, a SWAP happens to the color of the two target balls. In the figure, a SWAP has happened to the colors of all the target balls in the second row of boxes, but you can only see it in the colors of the target balls in the middle of the second row, since the others swapped color with a ball of the same color as themselves.

The next thing to consider is that by stacking boxes on top of each other, we can use the output of one box as the input to another. For example, we can stack two NOT boxes, and the resulting transformation is that the color of the ball stays the same:

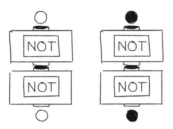

We can repeat this stacking trick to execute more sophisticated transformations of balls. For example, consider this arrangement:

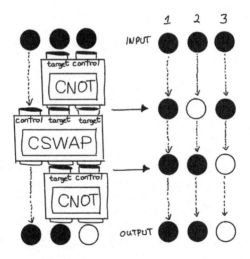

On the right, I have shown the calculation of the color of each ball progressing through the boxes, for the case when all three balls we drop in to the physical setup on the left are black. If we do a similar calculation for the other seven possible input configurations of three balls we find: (i) the first two balls always emerge the color they went in, i.e. their color is unaffected overall; (ii) when both of the first two balls are black a NOT is applied to the third ball. In all other cases the third ball is unaffected.

We could combine these three boxes into a new box, which we would call a "controlled-controlled-NOT" (CCNOT) box, since it applies a NOT to the third ball only when both the first two "control" balls are black. Because it is an important box, I recommend you write out a full schematic for the behavior of the CCNOT box much as I did for the CSWAP box a few figures ago. (Don't worry if you cannot, I will do it for you when we encounter it again.)

A twist on the balls

So far you could be forgiven for thinking that all we have seen so far is a bit of a silly game. Yet I'm pretty sure I can convince you, in a little while, that even the simple boxes we have already encountered are actually doing something interesting and extremely important, both practically and philosophically. Before getting to that, however, I want to describe one final box, a box whose behavior is so profoundly mysterious I am really hoping it will, by the end of this book, go much further. I hope it will completely change your views on what is "real" about the physical world around you.

Traditionally this last, very strange, box is named after a person who never built or even envisioned such a device and who has plenty of other things named after him. So instead I will call it the PETE box, after my friend Pete who has spent a significant portion of his life building and testing versions of it. Like the PETE box, Pete often does strange things—for example he put together a machine that enabled a tank of goldfish to browse the internet and control a drum machine. He made the profound discovery that goldfish like seeing humans without their clothes on.

The PETE box has only a single hole in both the top and the bottom. After playing with it for a while, we find that regardless of the color of the ball that we drop in, when it emerges from the bottom it is equally likely black or white; and from one use of the box to the next there is no pattern, no rhyme or reason, about which color the ball emerges:

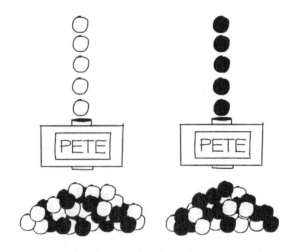

Is the behavior of the PETE box really so different from the boxes above? Of course the ones above behaved perfectly predictably, while the PETE box is unpredictable—which color emerges is completely random. So far we have deliberately not asked any questions about what goes on inside the boxes we have encountered. All we have considered is what they do that we can actually observe. As described thus far, however, the PETE box's possible inner workings are not necessarily particularly strange.

We can imagine building a box with an internal mechanism which flips a coin. If the coin shows tails, it lets the ball travel through directly; but if it shows heads, a NOT box is inserted into its path:

If this was the explanation of the inner workings of the PETE box, it would not be a radical addition to our collection of boxes. However, when we stack two PETE boxes, something remarkable happens: if we drop a white ball in the top of the first PETE box it always emerges white from the bottom of the second box. Similarly, if we drop a black ball in the top box it always emerges black from the bottom of the second box:

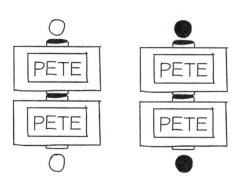

Can you see why this behavior is puzzling? It is critical that you do. The second PETE box, regardless of whether the ball entering it from the first box is black or white, should sometimes output a black ball and sometimes a white ball, because inputting a white ball leads to a random color emerging and inputting a black ball also leads to a random color emerging. But that is inconsistent with what is happening when we stack the boxes; stacking them leads to a completely predictable, non-random output.

After checking that each PETE box on its own is behaving properly, what is the next natural thing to do? Well, we get suspicious that perhaps the ball that enters the second PETE box has somehow been messed around with, even though we have exhaustively tested the boxes on their own and they seem to be operating fine. For example, perhaps the PETE boxes detect the presence of each other and change their behavior somehow? To check we do the following experiment. We slightly pull apart the two PETE boxes so we can shine a light through the gap. The light lets us determine the color of the ball emerging from the first PETE box, just before it drops into the second. What do you think we see?

We find that the ball that comes out the first box is half the time white and half the time black, as we know PETE boxes do. So it really does appear to be behaving normally. And now, if we let that ball we have observed keep going into the second box, it emerges from the second PETE box half the time white and half the time black. That is, if we observe after the first box whether the ball is actually black or white, then the second PETE box starts to behave unpredictably (randomly) again. It no longer outputs the ball always the same color as it was dropped into the first box.

We then turn off the light so we can't see the ball in-between the boxes, and immediately the two PETE boxes act perfectly predictably (non-randomly) again—a white ball always emerges white, a black ball always black.

Fine, perhaps the light is screwing things up? Well, we try many, many other less-invasive methods of observing the color of the ball after it emerges the first box, just before it enters the second. We find that no matter how smart a technology we employ, if the method we use is capable of determining the color of the ball emerging from the first box, then it causes the second box to have the random, sometimes-black-and-some-times-white, completely unpredictable output. If the method we employ cannot tell us the color of the balls (e.g. we use too dim a light), then they behave in the fully predictable way where the color that emerges from the second box is the same as the one going into the first.

We conclude from all this that somehow, just by our peeping, we have affected the process. It may remind you of baking a cake: if you open the oven door and peep in while the cake is rising, the cake goes flat; but if you wait patiently until the cake is cooked, it rises as it should. In that case we know the reason our observation changed things—we let cold air in. However, we don't know the reason our observations affect the ball between the PETE boxes. What we are sure of is we cannot be passive observers of the balls exiting a PETE box—and since the balls and boxes are ultimately made up of physical stuff, this becomes a realization that we cannot always be passive observers of the physical world.

This portends a major shift in how we view our interventions in the world. How strange is that? Well it's certainly a step away from the classic scientific view of the universe in which we believe we are not ultimately that important—and so can make sense of things either much bigger or much smaller than us by presuming they conduct their business in (understandable) contempt of our actions.

Later I will explain why, while such "observer dependence" is interesting, the fact that observations have consequences is not necessarily a complete breakdown of the whole intellectual edifice upon which science has stood successfully for centuries. (After all, perhaps everything we do is like baking a cake.) By contrast, such a dramatic conclusion is ultimately where the PETE box will try to lead us by the end of this book.

Another conclusion, almost as dramatic as the first, is that the PETE box's behavior portends a failure of the very logic that underpins how we think. This has exciting consequences. For example, it lets us envision radically new types of computers and other technologies—although in return it is hard to understand the full potential of these technologies, precisely because they don't sit well at all with our "sensible" logic.

Now it takes a few steps to justify this second conclusion. The first step is to try and express what we think is "happening" to the ball—what do we think is "really going on"; what do we think the "facts of the matter are"; what is "the status"? Or, to use language that is meant to capture all of these: what is the "real state" of the ball when it exits the first PETE box?

The word "state" is itself pretty loaded jargon to physicists, and later we will discuss some more precise notions of the state of a physical system. So far all we can be sure of is that the balls that we observe come in at least two distinct states, black and white. Other colored balls are possible to build, so to be cautious we try yellow, red, and grey balls (which are arguably something in between black and white). We find that PETE boxes simply don't work at all if we input any color other than either black or white: nothing drops out the bottom at all. So it is natural to expect that, even if we don't observe the ball when it exits the first PETE box, it actually is either black or white. However, if the state of the ball exiting the first PETE box really is black "or" white, then we have a black "or" white ball entering the second PETE box, and in that case the ball exiting the second box would randomly sometimes be black and sometimes be white. But it is not—this is the whole conundrum!

We are forced to conclude that somehow the logical notion of "or" has failed us. The other natural logical notion when faced with only two possibilities is to say perhaps the ball is black "and" white. Now intuitively this is nonsense—a single ball which is black "and" white is as ridiculous as a cat which is both fat "and" skinny. It is trying to combine two things that are mutually exclusive, while using a logical notion which requires the possibility that they are not.

Confronted with this conundrum, physicists simply invented a new word to describe the ball after it exits the PETE box. We say the ball is "black superposed with white," or more colloquially it is "in a superposition of black and white."

Superposition is a completely new possible state of physical being, and a completely new state of logical being, for two distinct alternatives. Sometimes you will loosely hear a superposition referred to as "black and white," but this is either ignorance or laziness. You know better now.

I will now step away from talking only about experimental observations, to explain precisely how our current physical laws describe such experiments. The first step is to find a way to represent superpositions—these new possible states of physical/logical being. The way we do it seems very arbitrary when you first encounter it, so first a small aside to motivate you to try and learn the details, rather than just skipping over them:

What follows in this book is the only option we know

What I will explain from now on is the only way that we have found to quantitatively describe what is going on with the balls and the PETE boxes. I cannot stress this point too carefully. Many people (myself included) have tried to devise alternative explanations, and often succeed in finding something that looks very different. Once we examine it more deeply we find, however, that it is either exactly (though non-obviously) equivalent to the description I will teach you, or it is in conflict with experimental observations and therefore worthless.

More precisely, what follows in the rest of this book is the only method known to work once we consider experiments that involve multiple balls passing through arbitrary combinations of the PETE boxes together with the CSWAP, NOT, CNOT and other boxes described above.

For the case of a single ball falling through stacked PETE boxes you can actually find other potential explanations which are quite simple. Here is one. Perhaps both black and white balls can have a small sticker on them that we cannot see, but which a PETE box can see. This means there are four possible balls:

white, with or without a sticker; and black, with or without a sticker. Perhaps when we create a white or black ball it also, randomly and with equal likelihood, either does or does not have a sticker stuck onto it as well. A PETE box changes the color of a ball if it has a sticker, and not otherwise. This means two PETE boxes either both change the color or both do not change the color—either way the output is the same as the input. To explain what happens when we observe a ball, perhaps our act of observation causes the sticker (if it is there) to be removed, and then randomly, with equal likelihood, a new sticker either is or is not added onto the ball.

I wouldn't waste too much time trying to understand how this simple single-ball model works, I am just telling it to you because it is possible, and so when you find something equivalent on your own please don't send me lots of emails telling me you've solved everything. Yet.

Representing superpositions, the new state of physical/logical being

To represent a superposition of black and white—and capture this new type of ambiguity between the ball being black and the ball being white—we draw a cloud into which we list both possibilities, separated by a comma:

Terry Rudolph

Because the terminology "cloud computing" is already used for something well-known (and irrelevant to our discussion), let me call this new state a "misty" state. (My father would say it's very *mist*-erious.) We could say, colloquially, that the white ball "splits" into a superposition, i.e. misty state, of both white and black.

Although the misty state seems to contain two alternatives simultaneously, we already know if we observe (look at) the ball, it reveals itself as only one of the alternative colors in the mist— and importantly, it does so completely at random. Thus, if we do observe the ball's color, the mist disappears and we get left with just a regular black or white ball. The ordering of the two color configurations in the mist is irrelevant, just like the ordering is irrelevant when you list all the possible things you might get given for lunch.

It may seem that we should use exactly the same ambiguous representation for the state which emerges from a PETE box when we have dropped a black ball through it, because it also equally likely appears black or white when observed. But it must somehow be represented differently, because it must capture the fact that after a second PETE the ball always emerges white or black. This means there must be some difference between a mist originating from a white ball and a mist originating from a black ball.

You could probably come up with many alternatives to distinguish the two possible mists diagrammatically. But, as mentioned in the preceding section, any method that works in general is ultimately equivalent to the following:

Here the black ball in the mist has a "−" (a minus, or negative) sign in front of it. I think of it as a "−1," a negative 1, somehow associated with, or labeling, this configuration within the mist. But it isn't a "physically different" type of black ball; if we looked at the ball at this stage we would just see it as randomly either white or black. No matter what we do, we won't be able to see anything to tell us that when it we see it black it is actually "negative-black."

After the PETE box outputs a ball in this misty state, what happens when we drop that ball (without looking at it) into another type of box? The basic rule is that you apply the box to each configuration within the mist independently. For instance, here is what happens when we pass the two different misty states we have just encountered through a subsequent NOT box:

The ordering of the ball configurations within a mist does not matter, and so the mist that emerges for the case on the left-hand side is identical to the one which entered. On the right-hand side we see the negative-sign labels can apply to white balls as well. The NOT box does what it always does—it acts on the color of the ball, and it ignores the negative sign, which just comes along for the ride.

To see how the negative-sign label affects things, we need to look at what happens when we drop a ball that is already in a misty state (having gone through the first PETE box) through a second PETE box. Following the dictum that you simply act the box on each configuration within the mist, each ball within the mist splits, depending on its color, according to the precise rules for the PETE box given above. This gives a larger bunch of alternatives within the misty state; a mist within the mist. Somewhat intuitively, we find that a mist within a mist is mist—the boundaries fade into each other. Here is the whole evolution:

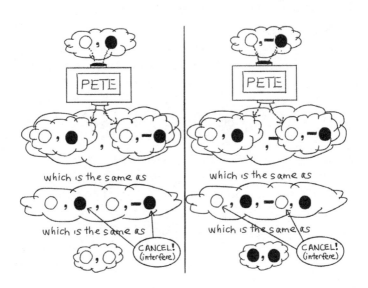

which is the same as

which is the same as

CANCEL! (interfere)

which is the same as

which is the same as

CANCEL! (interfere)

In these two figures we see the white ball split into a misty white and black ball, while the black ball splits into a misty white and negative-black ball. In the figure on the right, the ingoing black ball already had a negative-sign label, and when it splits that label is inherited by the whole misty state it splits into, hence the minus outside the cloud. This means it actually splits into a negative-sign labeled white ball, and a negative-negative-sign labeled black ball. Just like when your mother used the logic that if she makes two negative comments about the state of your bedroom she is actually being a positive influence, the two negative-sign labels combine to a positive label, which we depict as no label at all. What we see happen to the balls in the figure on the right is a bit like when we do math of the form:

$$-(2 + -3) = (-2 + 3).$$

Now, if it is ever the case within a mist that the configurations of balls (in this example we have one ball; later we will consider multi-ball mists) are such that two of the alternative color configurations are identical, except one has a negative-sign label and the other doesn't, then both of them vanish. We say they "interfere" or they "cancel each other out," like when we do math of the form:

$$+42 + -42 = 0$$

—except that the mist somehow describes material objects, not just ethereal numbers. We can see this happening in both figures above. In the left figure, the two black balls vanish in a puff of interference; in the right figure it is the two white balls that disappear. The only alternatives left in each mist are two configurations of the ball that are the same color, which means

21

if we looked at the ball now we would certainly see it as that color.

Putting together all these rules we can calculate the effect on a white ball falling through two stacked PETE boxes, which yields the "illogical" behavior that it always emerges white:

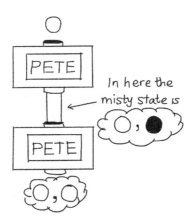

In here the misty state is

A very similar figure could be drawn for an initially black ball, to show it always will emerge black. I have drawn a tube to connect the two PETE boxes. This is because our act of observing the color of the ball burns away (destroys) the mist, so in practice when we connect many boxes we must use something like such tubes to prevent us looking at the balls before we want to.

Do not be distressed if the negative-sign is mysterious. My own mother, commenting on an early draft of this book, wrote: "I cannot get into the Why of that minus applied to a black-misty, seems so unfair but I am bashing on with the reading in rebellious acceptance, believing it can somehow be justified and maybe even explained!" Being confused by all this runs in the family.

Is the mist really a "state of physical being"?

Before moving on to examine the exciting power of misty states, a word of caution. The mist itself is never directly observed. I have called it a "new state of physical/logical being". However, amongst physicists these days the extent to which the misty state is "physically real" is very contentious. Everyone agrees that writing the mist on a piece of paper and using it to work out what we will observe in our experiments (performed with actual physical objects) is valid. So, in that sense, the mist is definitely a new state of "logical being" that somehow relates to a state of "physical being." But (a few? some? many?) physicists believe that the mist should not be thought of as "physically real" in and of itself. They would say it is only a tool for calculation—it is something we humans use to make predictions about experiments, and the PETE box should not be thought of as spitting out or responding to a physical misty state itself.

To perhaps labor the point, the mist in the diagrams above can be thought of as either (i) representing an actual physical process of some real stuff (drawn as a mist, but obviously not made of tiny water droplets) passing through the boxes; or (ii) "just diagrams describing an experiment" where the only physical thing is the color of the balls entering and exiting the boxes (once observed).

It is fascinating that we have this incredibly precise theory, which, as we shall see, is going to let us build marvelous new useful devices, and yet we are still arguing about what it all really means. My goal in this book is not to bias you on which side of the argument to sit. In Part III, by which time you will have understood all the key points of the theory, I will introduce you to some of the arguments for and against both viewpoints.

In Part I we will stick to investigating its awesome potential within devices that do not care about our philosophical consternations regarding how they work.

Computers without mist

Obviously our lives have already been revolutionized by computers and the many related technologies all based upon the same basic principles of micro-electronics. Pause and count the number of objects within ten meters of you which contain such electronics. In fact, in the interests of science, I recommend you grab a hammer, smash your TV or computer or phone, and dig out some of those little black "computer chips." Inside those tiny devices electric currents run around and combine together to produce the movies you watch, the game worlds you immerse yourself in, all the stuff you view on the internet, and so much more.

Yet what goes on inside those chips is actually just an electrical version of dropping black and white balls through the boxes we have encountered already—all the boxes, that is, except the PETE box. All the diversity of computational experience arises from electrical currents in one of two possible distinct states (a high and low voltage, but they may as well be called black and white electricity blobs) running through tiny boxes (etched into silicon), and coming out in one or other of the two possible states according to rules like those for the NOT, CNOT, CSWAP, and CCNOT described above. So I am going to call these non-PETE operations the "computer rules." The computer rules are simple to state, but they are what we call "universal"; from just this simple set of rules you can create the inexhaustible complexity of our computer-based technologies.

Seeing complicated larger-scale patterns arise from very simple rules for smaller patterns is neat, but perhaps not a shock to anyone who has dived a coral reef or watched bees work or crystals grow. I suggest to you, however, that a moment's reflection on the essentially unbounded potential of our computerized experiences puts into perspective the much more limited scope of examples of this kind from nature. Moreover, there is a really rather beautiful fact about these small-scale computer rules: as intimated above, they capture primal concepts of logical thinking.

Logic from the motion of matter

If we replace black and white states of a physical material with our ethereal mental notions of "true" and "false," then these simple computer rules capture all the pertinent rules of logical reasoning. The simplest example is that if something is NOT-true it is false, and we have already encountered the NOT box which negates "true" (a black ball) by changing it to "false" (a white ball) and vice versa.

For the next simplest example of logical reasoning, we need the CCNOT box, which we first saw constructed by stacking a CNOT, a CSWAP and another CNOT:

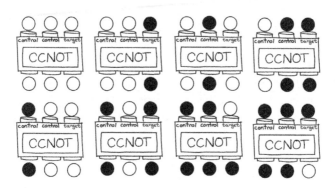

(In the Summary of Part I is a diagram recalling how every box works in case you find it difficult to remember them).

The CCNOT box's logical specialty is AND: If two statements are true, we can say "statement 1 AND statement 2 is true" but not otherwise. The CCNOT box computes the AND of the first two balls as follows: if we input a white ball into the third hole, then it emerges black (i.e. true) if and only if both ball 1 *and* ball 2 are black (i.e. true). This matches/computes the logical notion of "and" perfectly.

Another simple logical construction is that if one or the other or both of two statements are true we can say "statement 1 OR statement 2 is true." The CCNOT— with a black ball input into the third hole, and NOT boxes placed above the first and second holes—will also compute the OR of balls 1 and 2 onto the third ball. That is, the third ball will emerge black if either, or both, of the first two balls are black.

Slightly more complicated constructions give us ways of computing crucial logical elements like "IF statement 1 is true THEN statement 2 is true." Almost everything we ever try to explain or discuss or argue about is built from applying these sorts of basic logical constructions to facts/assertions/propositions we take to be fundamentally (or self-evidently) true or false.

We have very briefly seen then that both our (dumb?) computers and our (intelligent?) logical thought processes share a common set of fundamental rules, rules that can be captured by simple motions of matter such as balls passing through the computer-rules boxes. The power of computers that can make use of misty states by incorporating the PETE box is precisely that they go beyond our standard logic. They bring a radically new element into the computers—a radically new logical alternative that is not a natural part of our reasoning. As exciting as this is, it makes it very tricky for us humans to comprehend, encumbered as we are to think "computer-logically."

Mist through computer-rules boxes

Once we allow the strange logic of the PETE boxes—or equivalently the strange possibility of creating misty states—into our computers, then our whole description of a computation changes dramatically. Computers operating without PETE boxes I will refer to as "regular."

Without any PETE boxes, a regular computer made from balls is always in a single physical configuration of black and white balls. This configuration evolves to a single new configuration as the balls drop through boxes obeying the computer rules of logic. Given the input configuration of ball colors we can readily deduce the output configuration by applying the computer rules.

So far the only misty states we have considered were comprised of a single ball, but it is possible to create multi-ball misty states. The first step to understanding misty computation is to learn what happens when we use the computer-rules boxes with multiple balls in a misty state. To determine how they transform, we work out independently how each configuration within the mist transforms, and add the output into a combined final mist. Here are some examples of how misty states of two or three balls are transformed when they pass through a few of the computer-rules boxes:

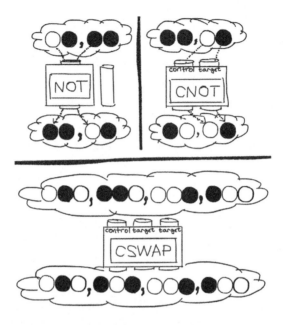

There are several things to note in these three examples. In the first, there are two configurations of two balls in the mist. I have indicated with dotted arrows that it is ball 1 of each of the configurations that drops through the NOT box. Ball 2 from each configuration drops through the "pipe" on the right (not indicated with arrows). That is, you take each of the two input configurations WB and BB (where "B" and "W" mean black and white) in the mist and act the NOT on the first ball to find the output misty state. I drew in the pipe, which does nothing to the second ball, to re-emphasize that no ball should be observed in transit or else the mistiness will be lost.

Now look at the misty state that is entering the CNOT box in the second example. In this mist there is also a BB and a WB configuration, but listed in different order to the first example. As mentioned previously, the ordering of the configurations is irrelevant, so this input misty state is exactly the same as the one in the first example. In this second example I have drawn arrows to indicate the path of both of the two balls within the second configuration; similar paths are taken by the two balls in the first configuration.

While the ordering of *configurations* (separated by commas) within the mist is up to you to choose, it is not the case that the ordering of the *balls* within each configuration is irrelevant. A WB configuration means the first ball is white, the second black, and this is not the same as the configuration BW. When we have multiple balls in a mist we always know which ball is which—this is the first (e.g. plastic) ball, this is the second (e.g. metal) one, and so on.

The third example shows three balls dropping through a CSWAP box. The CSWAP only affects the ball colors if the first (control) ball is black; if it is, then it swaps the colors of the second and third (target) balls. Remember it swaps the colors, not the balls themselves. In this example, this only changes the second of the four configurations within the original mist.

We see from these examples that passing a mist through any of the boxes obeying the computer rules does not change the total number of different configurations within a mist—it changes only the colors within the configurations that make up the input mist. Things are very different once the PETE box enters the picture.

Mist through both computer-rules and PETE boxes

Recall that every time a ball goes through a PETE box you split it into some mist. If a ball is already within a mist when you do this, then it splits up within the mist into more mist, potentially interfering (i.e., the negative configurations cancel with positive configurations). Here is an example to give you a picture to keep in mind. Don't worry at this stage if it's all a bit foggy and you can't follow the evolution through exactly; although if you can, that's great—you then can understand the rest of this book no problem:

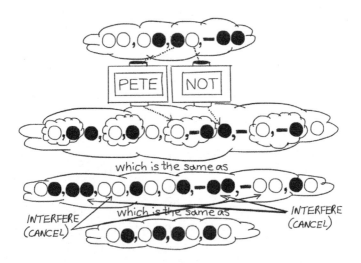

Within the text I will use square brackets to denote "edges of the mist," so the input mist in this example can be written [WW,WB,BW,–BB]. In this example, the first ball goes through the PETE box and splits into a mist of two configurations, [W,B] or [W,–B], while the second ball, which goes through a NOT box, does not split. Note that we then "expand out" the possible configurations. So [W,B]B becomes WB,BB for example. This procedure is explained in more detail in the next section.

In this particular example, if we observed the two balls prior to them dropping through the PETE and NOT boxes we would find any of the possible combinations of black and white with equal likelihood. After they come out the bottom we will only ever observe the balls to have opposite colors—the configurations with BB and WW were destroyed by interference. In the output mist, the configurations WB and BW are each repeated twice. This would be physically indistinguishable from a mist containing BW and WB each just once, since in both cases you have equal likelihood of seeing either color configuration, but I leave in the repetitions for pedagogical reasons to do with calculations we make later in the book.

Can you work out for yourself what the output mist would be if the input mist was [WW,WB,BW,BB]—that is, if there was no negative-sign label on the BB configuration of the initial misty state? You should find that one of the balls will always be a single color, while the other might be found either black or white. Note that it is only configurations of ball colors that can be destroyed by interference, not the balls themselves—if you ever find yourself with a mist containing no balls at all, or more balls than entered the boxes, then something has gone wrong in your calculation.

At any time in the middle of a misty computation, we may choose to look at the color of a single ball. In Part II, I will give the precise rule for how the misty state changes when we do this, as it is generally considered very strange and disconcerting. For the moment, however, imagine a computer which operates via a mist cascading down through many stacked boxes until, at the very bottom, we observe the color of all the balls. The outcome will be a random one of the configurations which remains in the mist (i.e., was not destroyed by interference). If all configurations remaining are repeated the same number of times (as in the example just given), then every configuration which remains in the mist is equally likely. I will explain the case of misty states where some configurations are repeated more often than others when we need it much later. At this stage the most important takeaway message is that, just as for a single ball, repeated configurations within multi-ball mists will interfere if one of the copies has a negative-sign label and the other one does not.

Collisions within a fog

The last important ingredient we need to understand about the misty states before we can see a concrete example of a computer enhanced via PETE boxes, is this: What happens when we bring together, or combine together, *sets* of balls—each of which are already in a misty state? How do we describe the larger mist that encompasses them all? Here are some examples from which you can try and work out the rule:

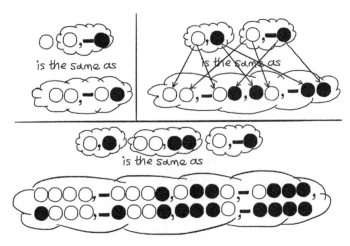

Can you see the pattern? The rule is that when you combine two separate mists you match up every configuration of balls in the first mist with every configuration from the second one and simply append those from the second mist onto those of the first, making sure to keep track which ball is which.

As the ordering of balls within a configuration matters, we must keep the mists all in the right order. In the third example, you can start by combining the first two mists, then combine the resultant mist with the third one, to yield the eight configurations you can see. Writing this third example out in detail:

```
[W,B][WW,BB][W,-B]
     is the same as
[WWW,WBB,BWW,BBB][W,-B]
   which is the same as
[WWWW,-WWWB,WBBW,-WBBB,BWWW,-BWWB,
        BBBW,-BBBB]
```

As you might imagine, the number of configurations can grow rapidly—every time you bring in a new mist containing two configurations, you double the total number in the combined mist. In the figure, the combined mists contain two, four, and eight configurations; continuing to bring in new mists each containing two configurations would keep on doubling the total: 2, 4, 8, 16, 32, 64, 128, 256, 512, 1024,... and these numbers grow very fast.

Interestingly, we see in the above figure that a negative-sign label applies to a configuration and not to a particular ball. That is, if you are appending one configuration to another and one of the configurations has a negative-sign label, you can put the negative-sign label on the whole joint configuration. For example, combining WW with –BB yields –WWBB. You do not need to keep track of which particular ball, or even which of the two configurations, the negative-sign originated from—

it is a holistic property of the combined configuration. This is similar to when we do math of the form:

$$2 \times (-3) = -(2 \times 3).$$

If you are appending two configurations that both have a negative-sign label, then, as we have seen already, the two negative-sign labels become a positive (i.e., no label). For example, combining −WW with −BB yields WWBB.

Although it sounds like combining mists is a physical process (grabbing the outputs of some boxes and smashing them together) in fact it is not. It is more like a bookkeeping device. It is completely optional if the balls you are combining are never going to both go through a box like the CNOT, for which they have to interact somehow. That is, if we have two balls in their own mists at widely separate locations we could keep them in their own mists, or we can choose to write down the combined mist. It is only strictly necessary to use the combined mist when the two balls are brought together and something happens to them where the color of one is affected by the color of the other.

Good grammar, is essential

A word of warning: a comma makes a big difference. It distinguishes a superposition (which lists different configurations of *the same ball* or balls), from a combination of mists of *completely different balls*. Here is a subtle example—compare these two very different scenarios, for which the output mists differ only by a single comma:

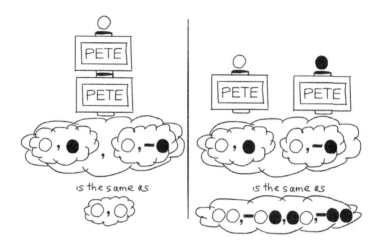

On the left we have one ball, which is in a superposition of [W,B] and [W,–B], and by interference it ends up in [W,W]. On the right we have two balls—the first ball is in [W,B], while the second ball is in [W,–B]; combining these misty states yields the two-ball mist depicted.

Lunchtime lesson

Should we find the rule about combining mists strange? In fact, it is pretty natural. Imagine you are going on a hike with two friends, and your mother packs you a lunchbox which contains either an orange or an apple. You don't know which; you only know your lunch options are "O" or "A." You now meet up with your first friend, whose mother clearly loves him more: she packed him lunch of either a packet of chips and a burger, or some jerky and a slice of pizza. Your friend doesn't know whether he has "CB" or "JP." (Yes, I know which lunch you want... concentrate please).

You decide to only carry one backpack between you, and

so you put the contents of both lunchboxes into it (without looking). The possible contents of the backpack are now OCB,OJP,ACB,AJP.

Finally, you meet up with the second friend. Her mother packed her a lunch which consists of either lettuce "L" or a tomato "T." And you thought you had it bad. After combining her lunch (still without looking) into the backpack, the possible contents you would all agree are now OCBL,OCBT,OJPL, OJPT,ACBL,ACBT,AJPL,AJPT. Note that, analogous to misty states of balls, the order I have listed the possible lunch configurations is irrelevant to the description of the backpack contents. But, sadly for you, the order of each possible foodstuff within any configuration is important—the first letter always refers to your particular lunch, for example.

Compare the eight possible backpack contents to the final example in the previous figure. The configurations match up if you do the following: identify the physically distinct alternatives of the first ball (white/black) with the physically distinct alternatives of your fruit (orange/apple). Similarly, identify white/black of the second ball with chips/jerky, of the third ball with burger/pizza, and of the fourth ball with lettuce/tomato:

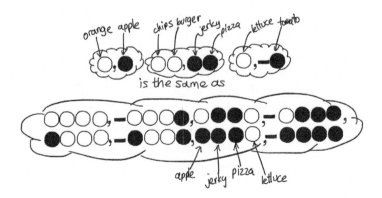

I described combining the lunches as a physical process—tipping the contents into a backpack without looking. But what if I had just said, "You each keep your own lunch; just list all the possible lunch combinations"? The list you would make would still be OCBL,OCBT,OJPL,OJPT,ACBL,ACBT,AJPL,AJPT. No "interaction between the foodstuffs" is required for the combined list to be the correct description of the full set of possible lunches. If your lunches were never to interact then it would be your choice whether to use the combined list or just list them separately. Imagine, however, tomatoes had the magical ability to convert an apple into an orange and vice versa. It then makes a difference whether the lunches get mixed together or not, because for something to happen (the killer tomato to attack your fruit) the foods would need to be in the same location (the backpack). The description of the (potential) ensuing mess—depending as it does on whether your friend actually has been packed a tomato—would first necessitate listing the combined contents. We could then describe the action of the (possible) tomato on the fruit much like a CNOT gate acting on the lunch list. This is all very similar to the case for the balls, where the combining of two misty states is not a physical process per se; it is, however a necessary description once the balls interact via one of the multi-ball boxes and we change a color of one ball in the mist dependent on the color of another.

As yummy as this whole lunchbox analogy is, there are limitations—there is no such thing as a "negative-sign-labelled tomato," for example. Moreover, we already proved (by stacking two PETE boxes) that there is no way to think of the misty state of a single ball as "the ball really is either black or white"; whereas the contents of your lunch box can be understood as "the fruit really is either an orange or an apple." But in terms of understanding how the configurations within separate misty states combine to make a larger misty state, it works perfectly.

Misty computation can be very lucrative

We are now in a position where I can finally give you a concrete example of how the addition of PETE boxes to a computation can be a huge advantage. This example is a little contrived, but it exhibits all the core principles that underpin the computational power of the PETE boxes. (We will incorporate misty possibilities into computers of the future to do much more interesting things than this.)

To set the scene, imagine you are trying to rob a bank. When you finally tunnel into the vault, you find yourself in a room containing eight giant gold bars. You have inside information that this bank has many vaults, and, in any given vault, either all eight of the bars are fake, or four are fake and four are genuine. The fake bars are very good, you cannot tell them apart from the genuine ones without extremely sophisticated laboratory-scale equipment, which of course you cannot just carry around.

The employees of the bank also cannot distinguish genuine bars from fake ones. Rather than give them a list of the genuine bar locations, which could be copied or stolen, the witty bank manager has installed in the corner of the vault one of our black and white ball computers, labelled *Archimedes*. Every bar in the room has a location uniquely identified by a combination of black and white circles, like this:

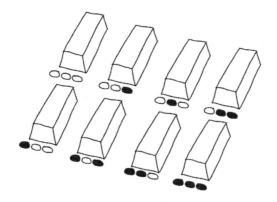

To check whether a particular bar is genuine or not, a bank employee drops three balls, with colors corresponding to that bar's location, into Archimedes, and a fourth "target" ball which starts off black:

Archimedes works in such a way that if the gold bar at the location corresponding to the input balls is genuine, then a NOT is applied to the target ball. So, if the target comes out white then the employee knows that particular bar is genuine, if it remains black it is fake. The three location balls just emerge the same color they entered—similar to the control ball(s) of a CNOT or CSWAP or CCNOT box.

Imagine you know that this is how Archimedes works, but

there is a snag. The time it takes for the balls to fall through Archimedes is very long—let's say an hour. Perhaps this is an extra layer of safety for the bank to thwart people like you, or perhaps it is because inside Archimedes are a huge number of boxes executing some very complicated computation (otherwise possibly you would just smash Archimedes open to see if the information you need is easily accessible!). You definitely do not have time to check more than one bar before you had better get the heck out of the vault. To make matters worse, you are part of a gang, which has busted open many of the vaults. The gang leader has declared that anyone who steals only fake bars will be executed, as they will have wasted valuable space in the getaway truck.

It would seem the best thing you can do is pick one bar location at random and check if it is genuine or fake. If it is genuine, that's great—you know you are in a vault with four genuine bars, and so stealing all eight bars is worthwhile. If it is fake, however, you will still be unsure which type of vault you have entered, it could be of either type. Without PETE boxes this really is the best you can do. Using Archimedes only once you can never be sure that you will be sure in an hour about which type of vault you are in.

Fortunately for you, and also for me (if you paid for it—though given your current escapade this seems unlikely), you have read this book and came prepared with some PETE boxes. This is going to let you determine for absolute sure which type of vault you are in, using Archimedes only once—that is, in just one hour.

The method to achieve this little piece of magic is as follows. You place four PETE boxes above all four entrance holes to Archimedes, and three PETE boxes at the bottom where the first three location balls emerge (there is no need to put a PETE box below the target hole). You drop into the first three PETE boxes a white ball, and into the fourth PETE box above the target hole, you drop a black ball.

One hour later, when the balls emerge, you check the color of the first three location balls. If all three balls are white then you are 100% guaranteed that you are in a vault containing only fake bars. If any (or all) of the first three balls are black, you are 100% guaranteed that you are in a vault containing four genuine bars and four fake bars.

To see that these last two assertions are true is a little bit of a messy calculation, I suspect it will be the messiest in the whole book, and so you should definitely skip it on a first reading if you're not yet comfortable with these misty-state manipulations. Although the calculation is messy, it does not use any new rules beyond those I have already introduced you to.

Before you skip ahead, here is the intuitive description of how it works. The three PETE boxes above the location holes create a large misty state, in which all eight possible gold bar locations appear (all without a negative-sign label). The target ball enters Archimedes in a misty state of white and a negative-black. Archimedes performs a calculation in the mist that acts on all possible location configurations at the same time. This is one part of the magic—a regular computer cannot do anything like this. The last three PETE boxes at the bottom of the computer are there to cause interference—the adding and subtracting of some of the configurations in the mist because of the negative signs. The interference is carefully tailored in just the right way such that the only possible way the first three balls end up white (the same color they went in) is if all the bars are fake; if four of the bars are genuine then at least one of the three location balls will come out flipped to black.

You didn't have to initially use three white balls at the location holes. If you begin with a different initial color configuration then you will find those three balls definitely emerge the same configuration they went in if all bars are fake, and definitely emerge in one of the many other color configurations if four of the bars are genuine.

The Archimedes calculation (consider this an aside)

We drop a white ball in the three PETE boxes above the location holes, and a black ball in the one above the target hole.

Case 1. All bars fake: If you are in a vault that only contains fake bars then Archimedes does nothing to the misty state; its effect is the same as if it was not there at all. After an hour the three location balls that exit Archimedes then each go through another PETE box. As we have seen, the combination of two PETE boxes in succession is the same as doing nothing—a white will emerge white, a black will emerge black. Since we input three white balls, we conclude that if you are in a vault containing only fake bars, you will definitely see the first three balls come out white.

Case 2. Four genuine bars: After entering the first line of four PETE boxes the balls are in the misty state:

$$[W,B] [W,B] [W,B] [W,-B]$$

By the rules for combining mists, this is the same as a single large mist of 16 configurations.

```
    The mist after 4 PETE boxes,
       but before Archimedes:
     [WWWW,  WWBW,  WBWW,  WBBW,
       BWWW,  BWBW,  BBWW,  BBBW,
      -WWWB,-WWBB,-WBWB,-WBBB,
      -BWWB,-BWBB,-BBWB,-BBBB]
```

This misty state now goes through Archimedes, which applies a NOT whenever the first three balls correspond to the locations of genuine bars. To illustrate, let me just pick four such locations at random. Let's say the four genuine bars are at the locations labelled WWB, WBW, BWB and BBB.

```
      The mist after Archimedes,
     before the final PETE boxes:
      [WWWW,  WWB**B**,  WBW**B**,  WBBW,
        BWWW,  BWB**B**,  BBWW,  BBB**B**,
       -WWWB,-WWB**W**,-WBW**W**,-WBBB,
       -BWWB,-BWB**W**,-BBWB,-BBB**W**]
        which is the same as
```

```
[WWW,-WWB,-WBW,WBB,
 BWW,-BWB,BBW,-BBB] [W,-B]
```

To make it easier to see what's going on I used bold font to indicate the target ball colors that Archimedes flipped by applying a NOT. We see that the configurations corresponding to locations which contain a genuine bar now have a negative-sign label. Unfortunately, the negative signs cannot be observed, and so if we destroyed the mist by observing the balls now we would learn nothing useful. The final three PETE boxes are going to help cause interference so that these negative-sign labels have some useful effect.

It is a fortunate happenstance for this particular problem that the full mist of sixteen configurations can be split back apart into a mist of the location balls containing eight configurations, and a mist of the target ball containing just two. This will simplify the analysis, but in general this kind of thing does not happen in a misty computer (although for this particular problem it would happen no matter which four locations I had chosen to contain genuine bars).

We now take this mist of the eight configurations for the location balls and send each ball through another PETE box. Can you see what a giant mist this is going to produce? For example, just the BBW configuration in the mist will break up into eight configurations like this:

```
            BBW
evolves through 3 PETE boxes to
       [W,-B][W,-B][W,B]
     which is the same as
[WWW,WWB,-WBW,-WBB,-BWW,-BWB,BBW,BBB]
```

Thus the total mist of the location balls, after evolving through the second set of PETE boxes, potentially has 8x8=64 configurations in it—although many of these will disappear due to interference. Here then is then a calculation of the full set of final configurations in the mist. Don't say I never do anything for you (and if you are reading this electronically you may want to resize the font to make this palatably line up):

```
[WWW,-WWB,-WBW,WBB,BWW,-BWB,BBW,-BBB]
      evolves through 3 PETE boxes to:
 [WWW,  WWB,  WBW,  WBB,  BWW,  BWB,  BBW,  BBB,
 -WWW,  WWB,-WBW,  WBB,-BWW,  BWB,-BBW,  BBB,
 -WWW,-WWB,  WBW,  WBB,-BWW,-BWB,  BBW,  BBB,
  WWW,-WWB,-WBW,  WBB,  BWW,-BWB,-BBW,  BBB,
  WWW,  WWB,  WBW,  WBB,-BWW,-BWB,-BBW,-BBB,
 -WWW,  WWB,-WBW,  WBB,  BWW,-BWB,  BBW,-BBB,
  WWW,  WWB,-WBW,-WBB,-BWW,-BWB,  BBW,  BBB,
 -WWW,  WWB,  WBW,-WBB,  BWW,-BWB,-BBW,  BBB]
```

In the large output mist the first line originates from the WWW, the second from the –WWB and so on. If you look at the 64 configurations in the final mist, you see that there are exactly the same number of WWW configurations with a positive label as a negative-sign one. This means they all disappear by interference. Which in turn means when you observe the three location balls you will definitely *not* see all three of them white. At least one of them will be black.

Even if you raced through all that (as I would do on a first reading) and didn't really follow it, that's OK. The final claim is that the only way to see all three location balls emerge white is for you to be in a vault containing all fake bars. Conversely, if any or all of the balls come out black when you observe them, then you are in a vault containing four genuine bars.

If you have the fortitude, it would be a good idea to redo this calculation for yourself, picking a different four locations for the genuine bars than the ones I chose.

Before leaving this complicated aside aside, let me remark that it is just as annoying for me as it is for you that I have had to describe this whole Archimedes problem and its solution in terms of the individual boxes and what they do on specific ball configurations. It is much like if we wanted to play a computer game but first needed to specify how each individual transistor within the computer should be set. In practice, for regular computers we have programs built via programming languages which let us determine what the computer should do by giving it a set of instructions that we ourselves can understand quite naturally. Unfortunately, we have no good programming language for a misty computer. This is not because we don't want one. So why haven't we made one? Well, if you have ever written some computer code you know that a program is just a set of logical instructions for the computer to follow; instructions of the form "check IF this thing AND NOT that thing are the same, and if they are THEN do the following." But that is all just a phrasing of regular logic, amenable to boxes obeying the computer rules—rules that we cannot use naturally to describe a misty computer!

Is there no limit to the magic?

I phrased the story above in terms of a vault containing eight bars. If there were double this number of bars, then the sixteen location labels would require four circles, and Archimedes would have four location holes. Yet, as long as you had the extra PETE boxes for the extra access into Archimedes you would still be able to determine the type of vault you were in by using Archimedes just once. This remains true whether the vault has 8 or 16 or 32 or 64 or… or 1024, or 2048, or …. or 65536 or… or any such "doubling number" of gold bars. In just one hour you can be absolutely sure of whether you were in a vault of all fake bars, or a vault where half of them are genuine.

Contrast this with the following worst case scenario. You enter a vault with 65,536 bars, and you have no PETE boxes. The gang leader now insists you do not leave the vault until you are absolutely sure which type of vault you are in. Perhaps you have entered a vault of fake bars. You start choosing locations at random and testing them and Archimedes tells you "fake, fake, fake,…." Are you definitely in a vault full of fake bars? No, because you may have entered a vault containing 50% genuine bars and 50% fake bars, but you are just really unlucky and keep testing the locations of fake bars. In that case you would also keep seeing "fake, fake, fake,…" as the answer. Until you have tested more than half of the 65,536 bar locations you could not be absolutely sure of which type of vault you were in. Do you really want to spend half of 65,536 hours (nearly four years) checking? Jail would be way more fun.

This last example brings home a crucial distinction between regular computers and those, like Archimedes, capable of utilizing misty states. Because it needs a much, much smaller number of steps, we see that even a slow ball-based computer using misty states will be better than using the fastest supercomputers around, once the number of gold bars to check gets high enough. The valuable resource that these misty computers can save us, is "number of computational steps"—which in many cases can lead to a staggeringly large savings in the time it takes to get an answer. It is a common misconception that the misty computers will be smaller and operate with a higher speed than regular computers, but in fact we do not expect that at all. The reason we want these misty computers is because, even if their speed of operation is much slower, it is their fundamental logic which is different, and this gives them an unconquerable advantage for certain problems.

Another point to emphasize about the misty computers is that they are much more than just regular computers with some extra fundamental randomness thrown in. In a limited fashion, the Archimedes example shows that: random choices without PETE boxes is not equivalent to PETE boxes. Access to fundamental randomness does make regular computers somewhat more powerful, but they still cannot come remotely close to the power of the misty computers.

Misty computers will be very lucrative, but not because they will help us rob banks. There is a massive worldwide effort to build them because they will vastly outperform our regular computers for certain problems that are major obstacles to technological progress. Examples include calculating accurately the chemical reactions necessary to design important new medicines, or solving the equations that will let us design highly-specialized materials to harvest solar energy better, or speeding up machine-learning so regular computers become more intelligent than ourselves sooner, or ... well the list is massive, and I have heard the figure thrown around that over twenty percent of all current supercomputer time is spent solving problems that a misty computer will be able to solve unbelievably more easily and quickly.

However, the really exciting thing is not that misty computers will let us do things we already do a bit faster—rather, it is that they will let us tackle problems that at present we don't even bother trying on our regular computers since we know they are much too hard.

Yet, while the misty computers will solve some problems much more easily, the set of all "in principle solvable" problems is unaffected by the new possibilities of misty logic. This is another point that is often misunderstood about what the misty computers will and will not be able to do. They will not be able to "compute the uncomputable." The set of problems they can solve in principle is no bigger than the set of problems we can solve on our current regular computers. How do I know that? Well, above I have given you the full set of rules for how to compute what happens to the misty state as it evolves through the boxes. So you could just sit down with a piece of paper, and draw out the misty states, and work it out for yourself.

How much paper would you need? If you begin with a problem using seventy balls falling through seventy PETE boxes (and we expect to build much larger misty computers than this) then the number of balls in the combined misty states will be the seventieth term in the doubling sequence: 2, 4, 8, 16, 32, ... Assuming you can draw at most about a thousand balls on a page, you would need so much paper you would be able to completely cover the earth. Use just one more PETE box and your paper stack will be large enough to cover two earths. (And I think *I'm* sick of drawing black and white balls....)

More sensibly, you would write a program for a regular computer to do the calculation for you, and computers don't need paper. They can store huge amounts of data in the tiny chunks of matter that make up their memory. As impressive as this is, in the end it only helps a little—even if we turned every atom in the earth into a bit of computer memory, the computer would only be able to "write down" the misty state produced by fewer than 150 PETE boxes.

While there are some clever programming tricks that will optimize things a bit, and reduce the time and memory requirements from these naïve estimates, the upshot is that even using these tricks you would need an absolutely giant regular computer (as big as the universe for even reasonably sized problems) and very, very long amounts of time (more than the age of the universe) to work out what a small misty state computer will be able to somehow do on its own, inside itself, quickly and easily. In theory you would be able to do any computation a misty computer does, but in practice you cannot. Unless, of course, you happen to be The Spectre (who is immortal) during Crisis on Infinite Earths (so you have lots of space)—and if you are then it seems likely you have many problems of inconsistent logic on your mind; best to work on those.

A final common misconception about misty computers is that this huge growth in the number of configurations is "obviously" the source of the extra power of a misty computation. But some caution is required. If you went on a hike with seventy people, each of whom had a "two options" lunch which you threw in a backpack, the total number of potential lunch configurations in the backpack is just as large as the misty state after dropping balls through seventy PETE boxes. Just as for a misty state, when you look inside the backpack, you will only see one of the configurations. Within the mist, however, interference (cancellation) is possible between different configurations that are somehow all "in there" together, and this is not something that can be mimicked by your lunch.

Well, why can't we buy one of these magical, misty computers yet?

We can build many versions of the PETE box already, and our current computers already contain devices (transistors) implementing the computer rules like NOT and CNOT and CSWAP and so on. So why can't we just join them all up?

The reason we cannot just grab some components at Fry's electronics and hack up a misty computer is because the computer-rules devices we have built (so far) are all really nosy: they just can't help themselves looking at the color of the ball exiting the PETE box. We try and try to get them to not do it, but they are like a curious cat that desperately needs to see the color, and their observations keep on burning away the valuable mist. Nosiness leads to noisiness.

We are making a lot of progress, however, and I am optimistic we will create large scale, useful misty states very soon.

Many, many words ago I claimed the existence of misty states would profoundly change your whole view of the physical world. But with respect to computers, this now seems to be a bit of hyperbole, as if I was just writing a standard pop-sci book. I mean, sure these new computers will impact your life, they may even help extend it hundreds of years, but the progression of our lives is already marked by the continual increase in computing power we have all witnessed and come to expect. In terms of challenging deep-seated conceptions about how the universe works we are going to have to delve into a more detailed look at the illogical behavior of the misty states. This will show they are completely incompatible with "sensible and obvious" expectations we have about the nature of physical reality.

Summary of Part I

*   Two distinct physical properties (e.g., black and white color) of a system (e.g., balls) can be manipulated by extremely simple rules (e.g., NOT, CCNOT, etc.) that nonetheless

can produce the profound complexity of computation, and moreover map directly to the basic logic of our thought processes.

* There exist some experiments that exhibit fundamental randomness. The origin of the randomness is subtler than our simple ignorance about what's going on inside the experiment.

* Two distinct physical states can sometimes be in a misty state or "superposition," which is jargon for a new state of physical/logical being.

* Our observations of things cannot be completely passive.

* These misty states are definitely math and possibly physics, but their status is contentious.

* The misty states grow rapidly as you bring in more systems. But the same can be said about your lunch prospects.

* Regardless of what they are, a suitably built computer will be able to utilize misty states to do certain computations in vastly fewer steps than regular computers would require. This means we don't need to care about the speed at which they execute each step: they will win because they use a different logic.

* The excitement about misty computers is not because they will let us solve problems we currently tackle a bit faster, it is because they open up vast new territories of previously unthinkable problems to take on.

* Misty computers do not compute the uncomputable—the set of in-principle soluble problems is the same. They just make previously highly infeasible problems tractable.

* The boxes we have encountered are:

In the diagram, only cases where the output is different from the input are shown—in all other cases the boxes do not change the input.

Part II: Q-ENTANGLEMENT

A tale of testing telepathy

Many people—let's call them psychics—claim to have telepathic ability; that is, an ability for instantaneous communication between two separated minds, via means unknown. Whenever asked to evaluate claims of powers that go beyond the laws of physics as we currently understand them, the prominent magician James Randi (who in the past has offered a $1 million dollar prize for any demonstration of such) will insist the claimants first make precise exactly what it is they say they can do. He has found there is no point in designing the test and then challenging the psychics to meet its standards, because the psychics can wriggle out by saying their powers are not compatible with meeting the specific challenge the skeptical tester would like. Rather, it is best to test exactly what it is the psychics claim to be able to do, making sure only to install obvious and agreed-upon safeguards against cheating.

Imagine (as I hope is actually true) that you are skeptical of generic claims of psychic abilities, but you are open to being convinced otherwise by a suitably rigorous demonstration. You are working for Randi when two psychics, Alice and Bob, contact you (by regular means), claiming to be telepathic. You now enter a negotiation as to how they will demonstrate their ability. Unfortunately, and this is quite typical, they do not claim to be able to do something obvious and readily testable, like transmit a simple message. Their powers, they say, are subtler.

Eventually the protocol they propose involves them each being separated in well-shielded rooms, to prevent communication by any regular means. Within each room a tester will flip a coin and tell the psychic in that room the outcome, "heads" or "tails." The psychics will each then have to say to their tester one of two very magical words—namely, either "black" or "white."

Proposed test of telepathy:

The psychics win the $1 million if both coin flips come up tails and they both say "black."

There are two rules:

Rule 1: If both coins are heads, the psychics must not both say "black."

Rule 2: If one coin is heads and the other is tails, the psychic told "heads" must not say "white" when the psychic told "tails" says "black."

If either of the rules are broken, the psychics are severely punished.

There is quite a lot to think about in terms of understanding this proposal.

Firstly, the "game" will need to be played multiple times. If it is only played once and something other than "tails-tails" comes up, then the psychics have no opportunity to win at all.

Secondly, the proposal is that the psychics are "severely punished" if they break either of the two rules. What is something so bad nobody would risk it, even for a million dollars? Think of the worst thing that could happen to someone (head chopped off, pet cat skinned alive until it's half-dead, ugly selfie posted on Instagram—whatever). Are you confident the punishment is so bad they will not risk it for a million dollars? Less drastic would be to impose a proviso: if any of their answers ever break one of the two rules, the whole game is off, and they definitely lose. If it so happens that every time the game is played and they try to win by non-telepathic means, they also necessarily run some risk of breaking one of the rules, then by playing many times you can make it very, very unlikely (much less than a one-in-a-million chance) that they could win.

Thirdly, if the psychics are isolated and cannot communicate then the testers also are unable to communicate. So, they will need to play a bunch of times, and then the testers get together and compare the coin flips and psychics' answers in order to check if the psychics ever won (and, if so, did they also always satisfy the two rules?).

But all of this is jumping the gun a little. Why would they need to be psychic to win at all?

I would encourage you to stop now and think about possible strategies for Alice and Bob. To make it easier, here is a summary of the answers that are or are not allowed under the two rules:

ANSWERS

		Alice Bob B B	Alice Bob B W	Alice Bob W B	Alice Bob W W
COIN FLIPS	Alice Bob T T	WIN!	OK	OK	OK
	Alice Bob T H	OK	NO!	OK	OK
	Alice Bob H T	OK	OK	NO!	OK
	Alice Bob H H	NO!	OK	OK	OK

It seems like there should be no problem for them to win the game. But there is. You should try for yourself to prove that they cannot win the game while simultaneously always obeying the two rules (unless, of course, they are actually telepathic). One way to see the issues is to play out what you imagine the conversation between the two psychics will be when they get together to work out what they are going to do.

AN IMAGINED CONVERSATION
BETWEEN THE PSYCHICS

ALICE: Awesome, those suckers accepted our proposed test. Obviously we aren't actually psychic, but I'm sure we can win this game.

BOB: Let's work out a strategy. Actually, we both know I'm not the sharpest pencil in the box, Alice—I better let you work it out.

ALICE: Fine. By Rule 1, when we both get heads, we cannot both answer "black." So how about I will answer "white" when I get heads, and you can answer "black" when you get heads.

BOB: Woah, slow down there, Alice. I think I better write this down, it sounds complicated already.

Bob hunts for pencil and paper, finally finds one and draws a diagram.

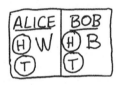

Bob shows it to Alice.

BOB: (*Proudly*) See, I made a table of what we should do. I drew a picture of each coin and its two possible outcomes H or T that the tester could tell us, and I'm putting B to mean black and W to mean white next to each outcome for what color we should answer.

ALICE: Yes Bob, it's very pretty. Let's keep going. Since we only win by both answering "black" when we both get tails, when we see tails we should always answer "black."

Bob duly makes a note of this as well.

ALICE: So there you go, we have a solution. Now, let's think about what to spend all that money on....

Bob is looking a bit puzzled, scratching his head. Alice has started to daydream.

BOB: Uh, Alice, I think there is a liiiiiittle problem. By Rule 2 if I get tails and you get heads I am not allowed to answer "black" when you answer "white." See, I put a line through the combination that breaks the rule:

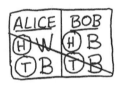

Alice slowly refocuses her attention.

BOB: And because you won't know whether the coin in my room came up heads or tails, there is a risk we will break this rule.
ALICE: (*Impatiently*) Yes, Bob, I see the point. Let me think for a second.

Both Alice and Bob enter deep concentration.

BOB: (*Eagerly*) Oh, wait, I have an idea—we can make sure to not break Rule 2 by using almost the same idea as you had Alice, except that I will say white when I get told tails. See, this is what I propose we answer, it clearly satisfies both Rule 1 and Rule 2:

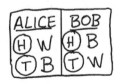

ALICE: (*A little sarcastically*) Sure Bob, that's great. We will obey both the rules. But don't you see a problem with that?

BOB: Uh, no, looks fine to me.

ALICE: Think, Bob, think. If we give those answers, then we will never win. When we both get told "tails," you will be answering "white"—and we only win if we both say "black" when we both get told "tails."

BOB: Oh, yeah, um sorry Alice.

ALICE: (*Muttering to herself*) For tails we both answer "black," but by Rule 1 at least one of us needs to answer "white" for heads, and Rule 2 rules out the other person saying "black" for tails, which rules out winning....

BOB: I can't think through logical stuff like you, Alice. So I'm going to draw out every possible way we can choose to answer, and then put a line through every combination that violates one of the rules.

Bob starts drawing and after a few minutes produces his diagram:

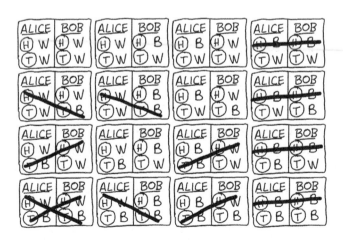

BOB: Nooooow I see the problem. There are some answers we can give that don't break any of the rules, but the winning combinations are the ones in the bottom row for which we both answer black when both coin flips are tails. All of those have at least one line through them because they disobey one or both of the rules.

ALICE: Damn, what have we gotten ourselves into? If only I were actually telepathic, then I would just telepathize the coin outcome my tester gets to you, and even *you* would be able to make sure we win. But I'm not telepathic, and I'm sure you're not, Bob, since it presumably requires having more than three brain cells.

BOB: Hey, no need to get nasty now. Even a three-brain-celled person can lead a nuclear weaponized country, you know.

Scene ends with two grouchy "psychics" not talking to each other, at least not verbally.

Let me harp on a little longer about the psychics' options if they are not telepathic. Perhaps it is a mistake for them to pre-determine their strategy? Maybe they should only decide on a "black" versus "white" answer once they know the coin flip they are told by their tester? For example, they could use a coin flip of their own and base their color choice partially on the outcome. Can you see why such a "non-deterministic" (i.e., not pre-determined) strategy won't help? It makes the other psychic even less sure what their partner is answering, and that cannot help them win. Even if their strategy is chosen randomly in this way, it will still amount to one of the sixteen diagrams Bob drew above, and so will either not have any chance of winning, or will run some risk of breaking a rule. Once again we see we need to test them multiple times to be sure they didn't just get lucky.

If the psychics are not telepathic and rather employ some combination of the strategies in the diagram Bob drew above, then whenever they cheat (by deciding their colors based on the last row in the diagram, which are all the possibilities where they both answer black for tails) they run at least a one-in-four chance of breaking one of the rules. You can see this in the diagram: for each of the enumerated potential cheating tactics in the last row, at least one of the four possible coin combinations makes them answer colors forbidden by the rules. They also have a one-in-four chance of winning, since this is how often both coin flips would come up tails. Finally, they have a one-in-two chance that nothing happens: they don't win (because the coin flips did not come up both tails), but at least they don't break a rule and get caught.

You and Randi don't really care what cheating strategy they would optimally employ—you just want to pick a number of times they must win, such that you and he can be confident that they would have less than (say) a one-in-a-million chance of winning unless they really are telepathic. Calculating odds like this is a bit tricky. They will need to cheat many times, and each time that they cheat and don't win they need to get away with it. Intuitively their likelihood of doing so decreases rapidly, much as the chances of you playing roulette and it landing on red over and over and over again decreases rapidly the more times you play. Fortunately, you have your friend in the bank, the same one who gave you inside information when you were robbing it in Part I. Unlike most people who work in banking, your friend understands this kind of thing. He tells you that if they win twenty times using any of the strategies from the last row in the table above, the probability they get away with cheating is less than one in a million. (If you want to see the calculation go to the webpage for this book).

You explain to the psychics that you want to play the game multiple times, both to give them a chance to win and to safeguard against cheating, and you require at least twenty wins. They come back and say that if the game is played four thousand times—so that by the law of averages the coin flips will both come up tails about a thousand times—they will definitely win more than twenty times, and will never break a rule in any of the four thousand games.

Once you understand all this you and Randi agree with the psychics that this is a fair test. You even get a bit carried away, and offer to also throw in a couple of genuine gold bars you came across recently.

CHALLENGE PROTOCOL:

REPEAT 4000 TIMES

1/ Testers each flip coin, announce outcome "heads" or "tails"

2/ Psychics each announce "black" or "white".

3/ Psychics win whenever both coins come up tails, and they both answer black

4/ Psychics lose if any of their announcements match the following
 "black–black" for "heads–heads"
 " black–white " for " tails–heads"
 " white–black " for " heads–tails"

5/ If the psychics win 20 or more times they will receive $1,000,000 and 2 gold bars

Signed
Alice 'Wonderland James Randi

Playing the games

The day of the test comes, and there is much fanfare as the world's media descends. Alice and Bob show up. Hang on, what is going on? They are both carrying a large number of boxes that they each want to take into their isolated room. They say that there is nothing in the rules preventing them having "telepathic aids."

Now, given more time and without the glare of the media, you would hopefully realize that you should contact me or some other scientist just to be sure you haven't missed something. But here is the thing: You and Randi are fully convinced that you have managed to completely isolate the two rooms that each psychic/tester pair will be closed into. What could it really matter if Alice and Bob bring some stuff in with them? Even if they bring in powerful supercomputers to help them do complicated calculations that might somehow help determine the color they should announce to each coin flip, you are sure from the arguments presented above that they cannot simultaneously obey the rules and ensure a win, and so they run a risk of being caught cheating. Of course, you do understand from your bank escapade that a misty computer can do some calculations faster than any supercomputer, but all the computing power in the world isn't going to change the fact they ultimately need to answer "black" or "white" according to some simple constraints that are easily shown to not be consistently achievable. So you decide to let the test go ahead.

Since you and Randi are the ones with serious money at stake, you have decided, as an extra hedge against possible cheating ("Hey skeptical tester friend, want half a million bucks and a gold bar?"), that you each will act as a tester.

When you get into the room with Alice you find that she has

brought in a huge pile of boxes, each labeled STORAGE and numbered from 1 to 4,000. You get a slight sinking feeling when you see that she also brings in a box labelled "PETE."

The test begins. You flip your coin and it comes up "tails," which you call out to Alice. Alice then takes the small box labeled STORAGE 1, holds it above the PETE box, pulls some kind of lever and almost immediately a black ball falls out from it. "My first answer is black," Alice tells you. You write it on the piece of paper you brought to record the coin flips and corresponding black/white answers:

The second time you flip it the coin comes up heads. Alice takes the box labelled STORAGE 2, but this time she does not hold it above the PETE box, she just pulls the lever, and a white ball drops out the bottom of the PETE box. Alice says, "My second answer is white." For someone supposedly being telepathic, Alice is acting quite brusque and business-like. "Next!" she says impatiently. "There are a lot of games to play."

After a full day, with the test drawing to a close, you have seen the same procedure repeated thousands of times. Each time you play, Alice takes the next unused storage box from the stack. If the coin you flipped shows heads, she just pulls the lever, while if it is tails, she holds it above the PETE box and pulls the lever. Either way, she announces "black" or "white" according to the color of the ball that drops out.

After the end of the four thousand repetitions of the game you and Randi meet up and exchange stories. He had the exact same experience with Bob as you had with Alice—Bob also based his black/white announcements on the color of a ball which fell out of a storage box, one that was first held above a PETE box if the coin flip showed tails.

You and Randi now sit down and start the laborious process of counting up how many times the psychics won. That is, how many times did they both say black when you two both flipped tails? You also need to check that their other answers obeyed the two rules. The first pages of your notebooks might look like this:

YOUR NOTEBOOK

Game	COIN	COLOR	Rules obeyed?
1	T	B	✓
2	H	W	✓
3	T	B	✓
4	H	W	✓
5	T	W	✓
6	H	W	✓
7	H	B	✓
8	H	W	✓
9	T	B	THEY WIN!
10	T	W	✓
11	H	B	✓
12	H	W	✓
13	T	W	✓
14	H	B	✓

RANDI'S NOTEBOOK

Game	COIN	COLOR
1	H	B
2	T	W
3	H	B
4	T	W
5	T	B
6	H	W
7	T	W
8	H	B
9	T	B
10	H	W
11	H	W
12	T	W
13	T	B
14	T	B

When you add it all up, you find that the psychics have won eighty times—which far exceeds the minimum twenty times you agreed on. They will win the cash and the gold bars! A bit panicked, you (not Randi, he's chilled about everything) do the comparison again—maybe having that overly-strong American Pale Ale while you were doing it wasn't a great idea, and you messed up counting? (For that matter, are you old enough to drink a beer yet?) You find that you were correct the first time, the psychics have exceeded the requisite twenty wins by a long way without ever breaking either rule.

The probability of eighty wins following a strategy where you risk a one-in-four chance of being caught every time you cheat, according to your friend in the bank, is absolutely and utterly, mind-numbingly ridiculously small. It is so small that you have a much better chance of winning a game where I take one grain of sand, mark it somehow, and hide it anywhere on any beach in the whole world, or anywhere in the Sahara desert as well. You then walk around the whole world blindfolded, sifting through all those sandy beaches, dragging yourself through that lovely desert, and at some point you grab a single grain of sand. The chance that you grab the same grain that I marked is still much greater than the chance the psychics can win the game eighty times and not be caught cheating, if they really are using one of the strategies discussed above and just gambling on not being caught each time they play.

I don't know about you, but if it was me I would be very, very suspicious at this point. Randi you can likely trust, although maybe given what is at stake even he should be suspect. Because remember, what is at stake is not just money and gold, it is something far more important: it's the possibility of some kind of psychic connection that defies common sense. Something at least as strange as telepathy.

But, in fact, stranger.

What went wrong?

Assuming for the moment you trust Randi, your suspicions will first fall on the isolation rooms. All it takes to win the game every single time is for information about the coin flip outcome in the other room to be available. For instance, perhaps hidden inside the STORAGE or PETE boxes is a cellphone of some form, which sends a message to the other room? While you have completely shielded the rooms to all known types of signals, there could be ones you don't know. In fact this type of cheating is not how they do it, and a bit later I will explain how we try to take extreme measures to ensure that it is not what they do, but first let us see how they really are doing it.

The answer, as you may have guessed already, involves misty states of balls somehow.

A tangled question: how did they do it?

Alice and Bob each have a pile of four thousand storage boxes (numbered 1, 2,..., 4000). Inside each storage box is a single ball. Each ball in each correspondingly numbered box—the one in Alice's room and the one in Bob's room—has been carefully prepared to already be in this misty state, where the first ball is in Alice's storage box, and the second is in Bob's storage box:

The storage boxes are very carefully designed so that they don't (even inadvertently) observe the color of the ball they contain. As we know, looking at the color of the ball will destroy the mist. Toward the end of this part of the book I will explain how this particular misty state can be prepared. One of the remarkable features of the mist is that, although the balls need to be brought together in order to create a mist like this, once it has been created they can be separated as much as we like without the mist being affected (as long as we keep all balls safe inside storage boxes).

Alice and Bob both get heads: When both coin-flips in both rooms result in heads, Alice and Bob each simply release a ball from its numbered storage box, observe its color (destroying the mist), and use that as their answer. As a result, they will answer WW, WB or BW with equal likelihood. They will never answer BB, since that is not one of the configurations within the mist. This ensures they will always obey Rule 1. They need a new pair of storage boxes/balls for each time the game is played, because the mist gets destroyed by the observation.

Alice gets tails, Bob gets heads: If Alice gets told tails, she passes her ball through a PETE box before she observes its color. Calculating what happens is simpler than some of the calculations in Part I:

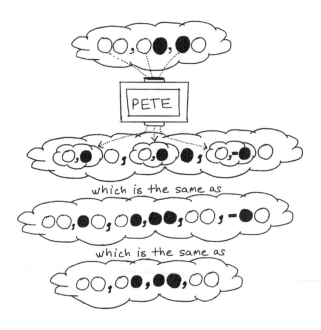

which is the same as

which is the same as

From this we can see that Rule 2 will be obeyed when Alice gets tails and Bob gets heads: the forbidden configuration BW does not appear in the misty state—it disappeared when it was cancelled out by interference. This means that when they now observe their respective balls, regardless of which answer they give (WW,WB or BB), it will be valid under the rules.

I will leave you to do the calculation for the opposite case—

where Bob gets tails and Alice gets heads. It is very similar, and for this case you should find that the forbidden configuration WB does not appear in the misty state.

Both Alice and Bob get tails: The most interesting case—the "winning" case, so to speak—is when both of them get tails. Writing out all the steps is a bit long and messy, but what happens here is the heart of Alice and Bob's "telepathy." Here it is written in our more compact notation from Part I:

```
The mist inside the two storage boxes
              initially:
            [WW,WB,BW]
Passing each ball through a PETE box:
 [[W,B][W,B],[W,B][W,-B],[W,-B][W,B]]
         which is the same as
   [[WW,WB,BW,BB],[WW,-WB,BW,-BB],
         [WW,WB,-BW,-BB]]
         which is the same as
       [WW,WW,WW,WB,BW,-BB]
```

That is, after both Alice and Bob have passed their ball through a PETE box, the final misty state is:

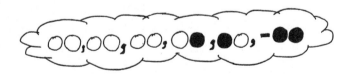

We see that the BB configuration is there in the misty state. This means sometimes they will observe both balls are black and win the game.

I have shown only the calculation for one pair of storage boxes, but the pairs of boxes are all the same and so, when the game is played many times, eventually some BB outcomes will be observed. Even just seeing the BB outcome once is amazing, given the fact the two rules are always obeyed.

In the above two-ball misty state, it would seem that the likelihood of seeing the BB outcome is one in six, because there are six configurations in the mist. It is not—there is a subtlety to do with computing probabilities in cases where some configurations appear more often than others (as here, where WW appears three times while WB, BW and BB each appear only once). At the end of this part of the book I will show you how to do that type of calculation and we will find it is a one-in-twelve (about 8%) probability of seeing BB, given two balls in the misty state above. For the moment, let us just be amazed it happens at all, because we couldn't come up with a strategy to win the game, and so just saying, "Oh, well, the psychics use magical misty states of balls," only defers the question: How do the balls actually manage to do it? Unless, of course, the balls themselves are telepathic—that is, they somehow know what is happening to the other ball?

Now you know how the psychics "cheated" you out of Randi's money and your gold. But didn't they do it in a remarkable way? It's worth at least a million dollars to understand this feature of the universe (and if it's the first time you have genuinely understood it, please feel free to post me a cheque!). In fact, the more one thinks about what has happened, the more disconcerted one gets. Let us delve a bit further into the conceptual problems that all this raises about how the world works.

Nonlocality of correlations

We have seen above a demonstration of what physicists call "nonlocality": When we observe a misty state of a ball in one location, the outcome of that observation can depend on what is happening to another ball in a different location.

The words "can depend" in the preceding sentence invoke a notion of causality—what Alice is doing to the one ball is "directly affecting" Bob's ball, or vice versa. For a number of reasons, this description is already controversial and not accepted by all physicists. One of those reasons is that there is no need for Alice and Bob to observe their balls at exactly the same time, and so which direction the cause happens seems to somewhat arbitrarily depend on the timing of who measured first.

A less arguable way of describing the situation would be: the outcome obtained when we observe a misty state of a ball in one location is inextricably linked with what is happening to another ball in a different location. Even the words "what is happening to" in the preceding sentence would make some physicists uncomfortable.

I don't think anyone would argue with this version: the outcome obtained when we observe a misty state of a ball in one location is inextricably linked with the outcome obtained when we observe another ball in a different location. This is purely a statement about the experiments we do. Just re-imagine the combination of Alice+tester and Bob+tester as merely experimental physicists who are choosing randomly between two different experiments to perform on their balls—either to observe them directly, or to put them through a PETE box and then observe them. They see are what are often called "nonlocal correlations" between the colors of the two balls at the separate locations.

Correlations per se are not strange. If someone gave Alice

and Bob each a box containing a ball and assured them that the balls were both the same color, then when they open their boxes they will see that the colors are correlated—in this case, both the same color. But in that situation each ball would "really have" a color prior to being observed; it is just that Alice and Bob do not know what it is.

Such an explanation will not work to explain how the colors of the balls can be correlated in such a way as to respect the two rules of the psychics' game, yet sometimes both emerge black when they have both been passed through a PETE box. Can you see why?

To perhaps over-labor the point, you can imagine that if the two balls did "really have" a color prior to observation, then they would need to choose their colors using a strategy that would mirror exactly the kind of thinking that Alice and Bob went through in the imaginary conversation above. Instead of giving black/white answers to heads/tails questions, the two balls are either being observed directly, or being passed through a PETE box and then being observed. But they still have to choose a color "to actually be" once they are observed:

AN IMAGINED CONVERSATION
BETWEEN THE TWO BALLS

BALL1: Awesome, those suckers accepted our proposed test. Obviously we aren't actually psychic, but I'm sure we can win this game.

BALL2: Let's work out a strategy. Actually, we both know I'm not the smoothest bearing in the barrel Ball 1—I better let you work it out.

BALL1: Fine. By Rule 1 when we both get observed directly, we cannot both be black. So how about I will be white when we get observed directly, and you can be black.

BALL2: Woah, slow down there Ball 1. I think I better write this down, it sounds complicated already.

Ball 2 hunts for pencil and paper, finally finds one and draws a diagram.

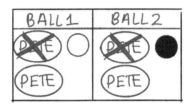

Ball 2 shows it to Ball 1.

BALL2: (*Proudly*) See, I made a table of what we should do. I drew a picture of each possibility—being observed with or without passing through the PETE box first, and I'm drawing a black circle to mean "be black" and a white one to mean "be white" next to each to indicate the color we should be.

BALL1: Yes Ball 2, it's very pretty. Let's keep going. Since we only win by both being black when we both get passed through the PETE box, when we see we are going through the PETE box we should always be black.

Ball 2 duly makes a note of this as well.

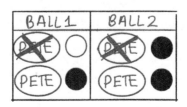

BALL1: So there you go, we have a solution. Now let's think about what to spend all that money on?

Ball 2 is looking a bit puzzled, scratching his head. Ball 1 has started to daydream.

BALL2: Uh, Ball 1, I think there is a liiiiiittle problem….

Hopefully you get the idea—if two intelligent creatures cannot work out a strategy to obey the rules but win the game (without being telepathic) then what chance do the two balls have on their own? Let me reiterate that explanations of the form "Well, we already know from experiments with just a single ball and a PETE box that we shouldn't think of a ball as really having a color when it isn't observed" are not particularly helpful in understanding the nonlocal nature of the correlations in the colors we do observe. Sure, the balls do not have to pre-decide which colors they will be, but we implicitly also granted that option to Alice and Bob—they didn't have to try and work out a concrete strategy beforehand, they could have said, "Let's just decide once we know what the coin flip in our room is." In that case, they would have needed even more telepathy to win once they were separated.

Causal nonlocality would have to be weird

Perhaps then we should consider more seriously the possibility that putting one of the balls through the PETE box actually causes, by some mechanism, the color of the other ball to be affected.

In physics, prior to encountering misty states and nonlocal correlations, it was always the case that the causes of things were mediated by "physical stuff." Sometimes the physical nature of the causal mechanism is obvious. When you grab your cat's tail and drag it along the floor, there is a complex story involving atoms and the forces between them that can explain the events that occur, right up to you getting scratched and later bleeding to death. In other cases, the physical stuff that acts as a causal intermediary is not so obvious. When you use your phone to call the ambulance for help (not in time, unfortunately) the radio waves that your phone emits and absorbs are not obvious to your senses. But they can be detected and manipulated—that is what your phone is doing—and they are so physical they can pull and push the molecules that make up a cat almost as well as you can (for example if you had, equally unadvisedly, tried to warm up the cat in the microwave). Radio waves are undeniably "physical stuff."

Events that are caused by physical stuff have certain common features, none of which turn out to be true for a mechanism that could give a causal explanation for the correlations between the colors of the balls:

(i) Causes precede effects, so the ordering of events in time matters.

(ii) If the cause and the effect are separated, then it takes time for the physical stuff that connects them to propagate. (You do not notice the time delay between when you speak in the phone and the person you are calling hears what you have said, but it is there. If you were on Mars it could take up to twenty minutes for what you have said to be received on earth, because radio waves travel at finite speed—the speed of light—and Mars is very far away.)

(iii) You can use the connection between cause and effect to send a message, though it will always be limited to traveling no faster than the speed of light.

(iv) It is harder to maintain the connection between cause and effect the further apart they are (the intermediary physical stuff inevitably "spreads out" in some sense and becomes weaker with distance).

How can we be sure that a causal explanation of the nonlocal correlations does not respect these four common features?

Going back to the story of you and Randi testing the psychics: we concluded that the most obvious explanation for their win would be that you and he have failed to shield the rooms properly, and they have cheated by communicating. On the face of it, there will never be a way to absolutely and completely shield a room. However, all known signals that can carry information also share common feature (ii), namely they travel at a speed no faster than the speed of light. This gives us a way to ensure that the psychics are not signaling to each other: You demand that after you tell Alice the coin flip outcome, she tells you her black/white answer (in effect the ball color) before there is time for a signal travelling at the speed of light to make it to the room where Bob and Randi are.

Because light travels so fast, even if you put the isolation rooms at the opposite ends of the earth there are only small fractions of a second during which the whole process must take place. I doubt you can even flip a coin fast enough. For this reason, when we do this experiment we use some electronic mechanism to do the coin flip and a different piece of equipment to insert (or not) the PETE box. That is, we use a mechanical version of both you and Alice. But in principle what we do is identical to the psychics' game—a version of it where and Bob and Randi play their part on the equivalent of Mars, safely too far away to signal to Alice.

The fact that nonlocal correlations do not get weaker the

further you separate the two experiments (feature (iv)) and cannot be used to send signals faster than light (feature (iii)) can also be tested experimentally. Both are also fundamental theoretical predictions of the whole misty-state description of the world, and if they proved to not be true it would be an interesting breakdown of the laws of physics as we currently understand them. Testing feature (i), namely that the ordering of the experiments in time doesn't matter, is tricky but has been done. I do not want to go into details, but if you know about the Theory of Relativity, it shows we can set up the experiments so that two different people will not even agree on whether Ball 1 was observed before Ball 2, or vice versa, and yet the misty states still correctly predict what happens.

The conclusion of all this is that if you want a causal explanation of the nonlocal correlations we observe, then it has to be a very strange explanation in its own right. So strange that physicists seriously consider other disturbing options. For example, one way to get around all of these conundrums is to propose that the balls (or the psychics) already know in advance all of the coin flips that you and Randi will flip. This explanation requires that no matter how you and he try to make an independent choice (you don't need to use a coin, you could use any object, or do it purely in your mind) whatever you will choose can be pre-known to the balls/psychics. This way they can easily arrange to obey the rules, yet sometimes win, with no need for telepathy or any other causal link between them.

Such explanations are known as "super-deterministic." They conflict with our psychological feeling of free will (which arguably need not be given much credence in a theory of physics), but more critically, they conflict with the very notion of performing independent experiments to test and verify our fundamental ideas and theories. Without such independence we have to call into question the whole process of science and, at some level, all the scientific understanding we (think we) have gained, because it is so tied up with that process. It is a significant price, but an idea that is considered seriously.

All of which is not to say that a causal explanation is impossible. One such explanation is to consider the mist itself as "real physical stuff." So far, the mist has only played a role of encapsulating rules by which we can calculate what we will eventually observe. It has been part of our mental deduction process—a mathematical object, not a physical one. As is hopefully clear from Part I, we do not see actual mist emerging from the bottom of the boxes. But one option is to take seriously the possibility that the mist directly represents some kind of real physical object, like a radio wave or a bowl of soup, and when we separate the psychics the mist is stretched between them:

Such a mist would, for the reasons just discussed, have to have many physical properties that differ from any other kind of physical stuff we have ever encountered. It would be arbitrarily stretchable and move instantaneously when you whack it at one end, for example. The whole question of how to interpret the mist—as something physically real? as something which is just mathematics in our heads?—is one of the major schisms between physicists. Some arguments for and against both are addressed in Part III of this book.

Before we turn to these questions, you are now ready to learn a couple more important features of misty states.

Computing the likelihood of observing a particular configuration given a complicated mist

Previously I skipped over explaining why it is that when Alice and Bob observe balls in the misty state

there is a one-in-twelve probability that they see both balls are black (and hence win the game). One would more naturally expect the probability to be one in six, since there are six configurations, but, unfortunately, nature is not quite that kind to us. Nobody really knows why. It's all part of the mystery you are going to solve for us one day.

The general rule for computing the likelihood (probability) of seeing any particular configuration is the following: Square the sum of the times the particular configuration appears, and divide *that* square by the sum (over all the configurations that appear) of the squares of the sum of the number of times that they each appear.

Huh? Yes, I do enjoy causing you a bit of mental pain. It is much easier to understand than it sounds, and the best way to work out what is going on is with an example of a single ball in a misty state:

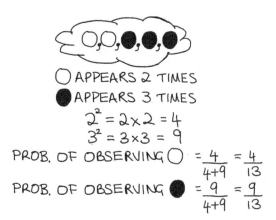

In this example the white ball appears two times, the black ball three times. We first square these numbers. The probability of any given configuration is then the ratio of the squared number of times it appears, to the sum total of all the squared numbers. In this example if you observe the ball you will find it white with probability four in thirteen (4/13=0.3077... so you see it white approximately 30% of the time), instead of the more natural expectation, which would be with probability two in five (or 40%). In these types of calculations, we ignore any negative-sign label—all copies of a given configuration will have the same label, since oppositely labelled copies will have cancelled out by interference already.

We can now work out the probability of the psychics winning the game, by calculating the probability of BB on the misty state that the two balls evolve to when both psychics put their ball through a PETE box:

OO APPEARS 3 TIMES
O● APPEARS 1 TIME
●O APPEARS 1 TIME
●● APPEARS 1 TIME

PROBABILITY OF OBSERVING ●●

$$= \frac{1^2}{3^2 + 1^2 + 1^2 + 1^2} = \frac{1}{12}$$

In the event (as always occurred in Part I of the book) that all configurations in a mist appear the same number of times, doing the whole calculation is unnecessary, all configurations are equally likely. Can you prove that for yourself more carefully following the "square divided by sum of squares" rule?

Making observations on a few balls within a multi-ball mist

There's one more rule for computing with misty states. Up until this point we have only considered the case where we always observe all the balls at once. The result of that kind of observation is that we completely destroy the mist. We are left with just one of the configurations from the mist, with a probability you have just learned how to compute. But what if we don't observe all the balls?

Here's a misty state being created from three initially white balls:

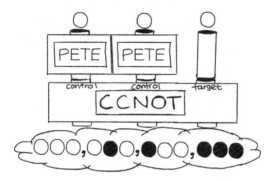

Have a guess at what the final state of the three balls will be if we now only observe the first ball?

As is typical for misty states, we will sometimes observe the first ball is white, and sometimes observe it is black. Let's say we observe it is white. We still will not know anything about the color of the other two balls. It is then perhaps unsurprising that the new misty state just comprises all the pieces from the original pre-observation state in which the first ball is white, in this case WWW and WBW. Similarly, if we observe the first ball to be black then the final misty state of the three balls consists of those configurations in which the first ball is black, in this case BWW and BBB. Summarizing:

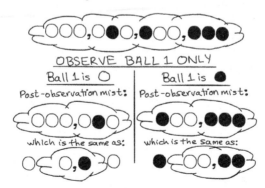

We see that by observing only one of the balls it is possible to leave the other balls in a misty state—whereas if we had observed all three balls, then there would be no mist, and no ambiguity about each ball's color.

Remember the two-ball state that the psychics used? Of course you do, it's how they cheated you out of your gold bars. One way the psychics can prepare that state is to observe ball 3 of the example above instead of ball 1. Summarizing:

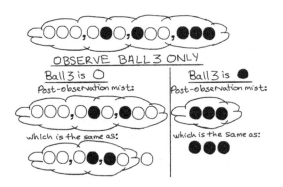

When the third ball is found to be white, the first two balls end up in the misty state that the psychics required. You should really hate that misty state.

Entanglement

Recall the following misty state that we first encountered in Part I:

This particular misty state has many beautiful features and is considered quite special by physicists, so I will name it the

"Bella" mist, after the Italian word for beautiful.

The Bella mist has the feature that it is reasonably simple to see there is no way to view it as being obtained by combining separate mists for each ball individually. That is, we saw in Part I that when you combine separate, individual, misty states of different balls you get a larger single misty state. The claim is that the Bella mist cannot be built up in this way. Here are three examples of two-ball misty states that are built up from separate misty states:

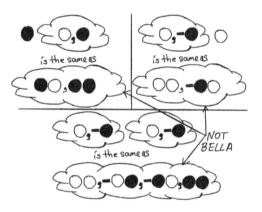

None of these examples are the Bella mist. The top two examples have only two configurations in the combined mist, just like the Bella mist, but one of the balls is always the same color in both. In the bottom example there are too many configurations. You should try several more examples to convince yourself getting to the Bella mist by combining two separate misty states is not possible.

This feature of the Bella mist—that it cannot be built from a combination of individual mists for each ball—turns out to be extremely special and useful, and so we give it a new word. We say the Bella mist is "entangled." As with the word "superposition," saying a misty state is "entangled" is just physicists making up a word to describe a situation which had previously never been encountered in any physical theory. Unfortunately, unlike "superposition," "entangled" is a word that already has colloquial meaning, and that meaning is only vaguely reminiscent of the precise way in which we will use it. This happens a lot in physics and math—common words get adopted for precise usage, and it can be a major source of confusion, so be careful if you ever study these subjects more deeply.

One might have thought that the lesson from passing single balls through PETE boxes was that, if you can't think of the color of a ball as something it "really has"—as a physical property—maybe the mist *itself* is a physical property. Then a single ball could "really have" a "value" of its mistiness. This view might lead one to think of superposition as the only mystery to be explained. The phenomenon of entanglement shows that this is not the full story—we have seen that an entangled misty state of just two balls like the Bella mist cannot be interpreted as arising from balls that are actually in their own individual misty states. In reality, superposition is not the only mystery.

Of course you may want to simply adjust the proposal; perhaps it is misty states of two balls that are the "real thing"? But then we can find entangled misty states of three balls that cannot be built from separate misty states of one and two balls. (Try it). The whole of Part III is about the many questions and issues surrounding the reality (or otherwise) of the mist.

A word of warning, determining whether a misty state of two balls is entangled or not is not trivial. Consider these 2 examples, which differ by only one negative-sign label:

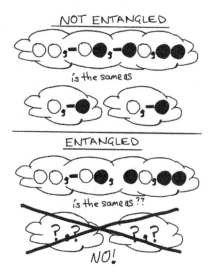

The two-ball misty state [WW,WB,BW] that was repeatedly used by Alice and Bob to defeat you and Randi is also entangled. In fact, entanglement is provably necessary for generating nonlocal correlations. It is not possible to generate nonlocal correlations with a non-entangled misty state, basically because without entanglement the balls behave as if they are completely independent. It is often said that entangled states are special because they are "non-separable." That is, you cannot any longer treat the entangled balls separately.

Again, some caution is required when trying to claim that this non-separability is fundamentally strange. Remember back when you went hiking, and your lucky friend had a lunch packed that consisted of either chips and a burger, or jerky and pizza but none of you knew which was the case? We could invent a way of depicting the state of your friends' lunch box, similar to misty states. Let's depict them in a rock (since they are more down to earth), and call them rocky states:

We see that by identifying foodstuffs with ball colors appropriately there is at least a superficial similarity with the Bella misty state [WW,BB]. The correspondence goes further: this state is "rocky-entangled." Specifically, it is not possible to create a lunchbox in this state by taking two individual lunchboxes that have uncertainty about their contents. More precisely, imagine you are told there are four potential configurations for lunch, namely CB,CP,JB,JP. You would say that is just the combination of two separate lunchboxes, one of which contains either chips or jerky, the other of which contains either a burger or pizza:

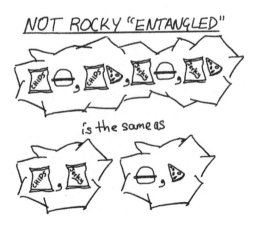

However, there is no way to create the rocky state <CB,JP> (using pointy brackets to denote the edges of the rock) by taking two separate lunchboxes in such a manner:

Creating an "entangled rocky state" like <CB,JP> requires some type of coordination, because some configurations need to be excluded. Similarly, creation of an entangled misty state like the Bella mist can only be done by causing the two balls to interact (perhaps via intermediary systems).

Once again, these similarities and analogies are useful, and perhaps (physicists argue about it) they reveal something important about how to understand misty states. But they should be treated carefully. If entangled misty states were really equivalent to entangled lunchboxes, telepathy/nonlocality would definitely not be demonstrated by winning the psychics' game, because Alice and Bob could have just played with their lunch and there is nothing strange about that. Your lunch cannot be negative, it cannot interfere, and it is not telepathic.

Summary of Part II

* We can perform far-separated, well-shielded experiments (observations) on balls in a misty state, the outcomes of which are inextricably linked, in as much as they cannot be reproduced by physical stuff (whatever it is) responding only to what is going on around it locally.

* Such "nonlocal correlations" do not depend on the temporal ordering of the experiments, cannot be used to send messages, and occur even if there is no time for communication at light-speed between the experiments. This puts them in severe tension with the normal type of causal explanations in physics.

* Misty states of two or more balls can be "entangled," by which we mean they cannot be treated as if they have independent colors, or independent misty states for that matter. Entanglement underpins nonlocality.

* Given misty states with unequal numbers of repeated configurations of ball colors in the mist, the rule for computing the probabilities of observing any particular configuration involves squaring numbers and dividing them. All a bit messy, but still just basic arithmetic.

* Beginning with misty states comprising many balls, observing only some subset of the balls can leave the remainder of the balls in a misty state.

Part III: Q-REALITY

Realism and physics

Science works, believe (in) it or not. Fortunately for phone companies the laws and scientific principles underpinning how your cellphone works are the same whether built by a person in China or one in the USA. Although you likely take this for granted, why should the laws of physics behave the same for different people in different countries?

One way to explain this universality is to posit that there is a deeper "underlying reality" upon which physics is based. More specifically we could presume that: (i) there exists a physical world that is external to us, and (ii) that we are not particularly important to what is going on in this external world—the stuff within this universe existed before we came along and will continue to exist once any or all of us are gone.

The extent to which we can draw "ultimately true" conclusions about this underlying reality from our scientific theories is debatable, tuned as the theories are to solving pragmatic problems for human-scale creatures. Still, one might think it unarguable that "there really is something there," and the fact that the human endeavor of science succeeds equivalently across variations in time, location and culture of the practitioner is somehow due to this.

The preceding paragraphs summarize a view known as (naive) scientific realism, of which there are multiple subtle variations. There are many, many people who would disagree with some, or all, of this view, both scientists and non-scientists. If you are interested in alternatives then start with the Wikipedia article on philosophical realism, and follow your nose until your brain hurts.

I am not qualified to enter a debate on such topics. My goal in this final part of the book is to quantitatively expose to you the extent to which the somewhat weird phenomena introduced in Parts I and II, and our physical laws that describe them in terms of misty states, yield new insights and conundrums on such questions, irrespective of your own philosophical preferences. Feel free to ignore any armchair philosophy that has crept in (I have tried hard to avoid it). I also don't want to get tied up in knots being overly cautious about language. I hope you are both willing and able to apply your own filters without rejecting the overall message, because the quantitative and technical things that you are now able to understand about our physical theories will sharpen your understanding of your own viewpoints; as well as, I hope, rule out some things you thought were obviously true.

Physical properties

If we at least agree that there are other people than ourselves (and frankly, if solipsism is true and you are creations of my mind, then you would all be better looking and made of chocolate), and if we also agree those people are experiencing the world in a similar manner to ourselves (again, you will find people who make a big deal of the fact that this is unprovable), then the consistency of our conversations about what we are individually experiencing ("it's hot," "that book is heavy") leads us to implicitly or explicitly form the useful notion that "things have physical properties."

We all appreciate it can be a blurry line between properties we know are subjective ("the banana smells nice") and those our common agreement indicates are objective ("the banana is yellow"). But it is a natural concept that there are at least some objective physical properties, of some kinds of material things, which are out there in the universe and independent of our subjective experiences. Similarly, it's a natural concept that some of those properties are more fundamental than others. Think of the incredible diversity of textures, smells, colors, and tastes of everything that we personally experience; all this originates from less than a hundred different building blocks we call atoms. Lego can't even make a model Millennium Falcon without double that number of different building blocks.

It is only a slight idealization to say that all theories of physics begin by stating the types of objects that exist, which is done by listing their fundamental properties. The ways objects evolve and interact are the basis of physical laws—statements about how the "values" of the fundamental physical properties change and affect each other. For example, if "mass" and "position" and "speed" are fundamental properties of a rock, then "a two-ton rock is located directly above your head and falling at a hundred miles per hour" is a statement about the initial values of those properties, from which you can deduce the exciting future consequences.

Originally our physical laws were based on properties we have personal experience with—we know rocks have mass, speed, position, color, texture, and so on. As time went on, we found that there are properties whose value cannot be experienced directly by a human quite so easily—energy for example. Typically, the properties are all interdependent—you can deduce the speed of the rock from its mass and energy and current position, but equivalently you can deduce the energy of the rock from its mass and speed and current position. Making good choices about the properties to take as fundamental is crucial to doing good physics—the theory of seismic wave propagation should not begin with considerations of the locations of individual grains of sand on the beach.

Correspondence between mathematics and physical properties

Our physical theories cover incredible scales, from the tiniest particles to the whole universe. The properties of the things at the smallest scales—the subatomic particles—include properties like mass, charge, position, energy, spin, etc. These would seem to be the "absolutely most fundamental" properties of the stuff that makes up the world. But the set of "most fundamental" physical properties keeps undergoing revision as we deepen our understanding, and this changes the terms in which we couch our smallest-scale theories. Often things that seemed absolutely fundamental turn out to be built up from more fundamental things, and so previously absolutely fundamental properties are now seen as derivative.

We infer new properties—and even the existence of new things—that we cannot directly experience, either by realizing that a good explanation of some phenomenon requires them, or because the mathematical consistency of some physical laws requires them. In either case the laws of physics are ultimately mathematical, and so for every object and every associated physical property "out there" in the world there is some kind of mathematical counterpart in our physical theory. The converse, however, is not true. Our theories can contain mathematical objects that we do not believe necessarily have a direct counterpart in the physical world. A subtle example, relevant to what comes later, occurs when you're about to flip a coin. "50% probability" is a mathematical object you assign to the coin's landing on "heads." It is not a property of the coin, it is not something that affects the coin's trajectory through the air, but it's manifestly useful to you predicting the outcome of a future observation. It is a state of your knowledge or information. While it may seem that such a subjective thing surely cannot be an integral part of a physical law, in fact the laws of thermodynamics have just such an "ignorance-quantifying" mathematical object indispensably hardwired in, known as entropy. Without entropy in our physical laws we would not be able to understand how the engine of your (future?) motorcycle works.

Sometimes, and this is where our story becomes interesting, explaining what we observe can only be done using some particular mathematical object, but we are unsure if that object is or is not in correspondence with some physical property. The misty states are the example we will examine in detail, because our whole notion of "what is real" and "what is really going on" changes dramatically according to whether or not they are a physical property of the world.

In order to appreciate the full ramifications of what we are going to talk about, I want to emphasize that if our current physical understanding of the universe based on misty states is correct, then everything you have learned about them applies equally well to all physical properties of everything that makes up the universe. The black and white balls (via which I introduced you to misty states) are typically composed from many particles, and their color is a derivative property. Yet their color can be in a misty state. To date we do not know of any physical property, fundamental or derivative, that in principle cannot be put into a misty state, and it would be mysterious if such a non-misterious property existed.

To refine some concepts and obtain some useful language we first consider a case about which there is no controversy, namely the distinction between states that are in your mind and the real states of the world when you flip a coin.

A deeper description of the rocky state of a coin

You might assign a coin you have just flipped the rocky state:

This is a more diagrammatic representation of the "50% probability of heads" you assign to the coin. It would be implausible to suggest that what happens to the coin when you toss it in the air is a result of the coin thinking to itself: "Now I should fly over there and land this way because I can sense that the weird-looking human over there thinks I play fair and is thus assigning me that particular rocky state."

A rocky state of the coin is therefore unarguably a state of your mind: a state of your knowledge or your information. It is a tool that lets you summarize your best predictions as to what you will subsequently observe. The connection between the rocky state in your mind, and the dynamics of the coin, is indirect. The coin responds to the "actually real" physical circumstances—the same ones that you believe are relevant but realize you are ignorant about, causing you to assign fair odds in the first place.

The real state of the coin—as opposed to its rocky state—consists of physical properties, like its mass, shape, color, height above the floor, speed and rotation through the air, and so on. We can make a simple diagram that captures all the possible real states of a coin:

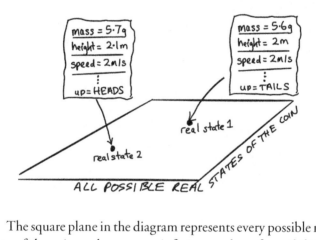

The square plane in the diagram represents every possible real state of the coin— there are an infinite number of possibilities. I have labelled two of them. You can imagine a piece of paper at each point which lists all the relevant physical properties and their values corresponding to that particular real state—the mass, height, speed and so on. One of the real states of the coin is whether the upwards face of the coin is heads or tails. (While it is spinning in the air there are fractions of a second for which the coin is "on its side," but to keep things simple I will ignore those.) Although I have represented the set of all real states by a square plane, this is just a schematic diagram. As more properties of the coin are included on each piece of paper that defines a real state physicists prefer to use higher-dimensional shapes to represent the set of all real states. This is because they like the representation to have the feature that two nearby points in the set of real states list physical properties with values very similar to each other. My drawing skills are not up to that, so you should not take the particular square plane I have drawn too literally.

Some of the properties of the coin—its mass, for example—stay the same when you flip it. Other properties change—for example, its height above the ground; its speed; which side faces upwards. In terms of the diagram of the real states of the coin, the whole procedure maps out a line through the set of real states:

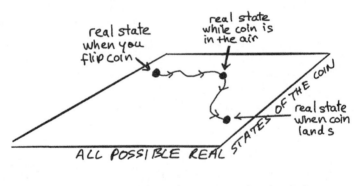

The set of all possible real states can be divided in two, according to whether the real state corresponds to the coin having heads facing upwards or tails facing upwards:

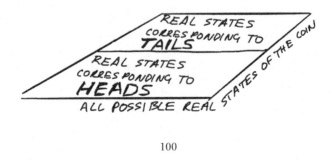

Flipping a coin is a game where you are being asked to predict in which of these two regions the final real state of the coin (i.e. after it has landed) will end up. If you knew the actual real state of the coin at the instant you flipped it, as well as all the physical laws governing how it flies through the air, then you would know whether it was going to land heads or tails. In practice, you do not know the initial real state perfectly, nor do you have the capability of calculating the trajectory of the coin fast enough, and so you cannot predict in which of the two regions the final real state of the coin will be.

However, at any instant of time, you do know some things about the real state of the coin. You know its height in the air is not a hundred meters; you know its mass is not a kilogram. All of those ridiculous options exist within the set of all possible real states depicted above. You do not, therefore, assign equal likelihood to all of the possible real states—that is not why you say the coin is fair. The reason you assign the coin the rocky state of a "fair flip," is that you are saying: "Amongst all the potential real states that are consistent with what I know about the coin once it has landed, half of them are in the region corresponding to heads, and half are in the region corresponding to tails." For simplicity, let's assume that—amongst all the real states consistent with what you know about the coin—you assign an equal likelihood to the coin "actually being" in any particular one of them once it has landed. To all the rest, you assign probability zero.

This state of affairs, then, is the more precise meaning of the rocky state—your state of knowledge. We can depict it:

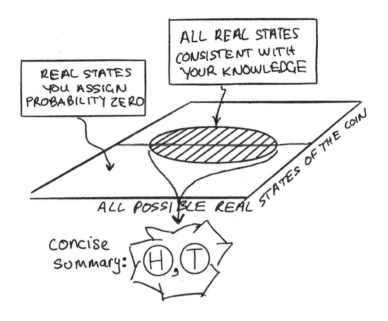

In the diagram, half of the real states consistent with your knowledge lie in the region where the coin lands heads, and half lie in the region where it lands tails. This is the reason you use the rocky state <H,T> corresponding to a fair coin as your "state of knowledge" about the coin.

The final lesson we can learn from the coin requires us to consider a situation where, for whatever reason, you think the coin is biased—say more likely to land heads. For the sake of sticking with a simple diagrammatic language, imagine the special case where you believe heads to be twice as likely as tails (i.e., the probability of heads is 2/3 and tails is 1/3). We could represent this new state, as well as the old one, in terms of both real and rocky states as follows:

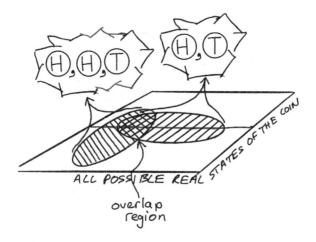

Because the rocky states are unquestionably representing our knowledge, it is fine to avoid the "squaring" rule that the misty states forced upon us in Part II—so, for this new rocky state, the two heads and one tail means heads is twice as likely as tails.

In the diagram, you can see a feature that will be essential to understand for much of what follows, so if you've started to drift off it's time to refocus. The feature is that there are some real states that are common to both of the rocky states. That is, there is a nontrivial overlap between the real states consistent with the two different (rocky) states of your knowledge.

This is not particularly strange in and of itself. To give a completely different example where a real state of the world might be consistent with two different states of knowledge, consider someone draws a random playing card and tells one person the card is red and another that the card is an ace. The two people have completely different states of knowledge about the card, but the "real states" Ace of Hearts and Ace of Diamonds are in the overlap region.

The most important point about such overlap regions is as follows. Imagine someone comes along and is powerful enough to determine the real state of the coin; that is, they find out exactly all the physical properties of the coin, including whether heads or tails faces upwards. If it so happens that the real state is in the overlap region, then they cannot tell for sure which rocky state you are assigning to the coin. The rocky state is in your head, and no matter how much they know about the physical properties of the coin, they cannot know what is your state of knowledge about the coin. This is true even if you narrowed it down in advance for them to just the two rocky states depicted above.

More subtly, the very fact that two different rocky states can correspond to the same real state indicates that the rocky states themselves are not a physical property of the coin. Remember, the real states are like a sheet of paper listing all physical properties of the coin and their particular values for a coin that happens to be in that real state. So, by definition, if a rocky state was a physical property then we would be able to look at the real state (read the sheet of paper) and know what the "value of the rocky state" was. Since there is more than one rocky state associated with real states in the overlap region, the value of the rocky state cannot be "on the paper" as it were—a rocky state is not a physical property; it is not (part of) the "real physical state" of a coin.

This has the following consequence: if, for some reason, we were unsure about whether rocky states were a physical property of a coin or not, then a proof that multiple different rocky states could correspond to the same real state would prove to us that they were not. Similar reasoning will form a crucial part of one of the arguments that misty states are not a physical property.

First, however, we delve into the simplest arguments that misty states are, in one way or another, a physical property of a ball.

Revisiting our first conundrum

When I introduced you to misty states I emphasized that the one thing every physicist can agree on is that they are, at a minimum, a practical tool for calculation. They work incredibly well— much of modern technology (transistors/computers, lasers/the internet) is built upon unbelievably precise calculations that misty states enable us to make about concrete physical stuff, that we frantically push together in order to bring you a better cellphone each year.

Let us revisit the first conundrum we encountered with misty states, namely that the output of a single PETE box is random, but of two stacked PETE boxes is not.

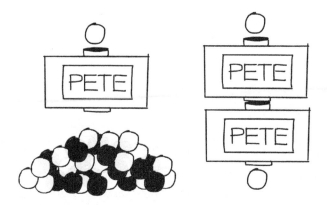

If the misty state [W,B] that we use to describe the ball emerging from the first PETE box (in the case where we don't observe its color) is an "actual real thing" or, alternatively, "an actual physical property of a ball," then it is plausible that the second PETE box can "see" that the ball is in a misty state—and, in fact, which particular misty state it is in.

Perhaps, unlike ourselves, PETE boxes do not destroy the mist by looking at it? If so, then the second PETE box can distinguish whether the mist is [W,B] or [W,–B], and evolve the color of the output ball to white or black accordingly:

Thus, by taking the misty states to be real physical things—that is, actual physical properties of the balls—we immediately obtain a potential explanation of (some of) the weirdness of the PETE boxes. It seems like such a simple and natural explanation of the PETE boxes experiment that you may be wondering: why is there any controversy at all?

Two variations on a misty state "being real"

The only requirement for the explanation in the preceding section to work is that the PETE boxes be able to "see," one way or another, exactly what the misty state of the ball is. We would like to say this sort of explanation relies on the misty state "being real," or "being a physical property" such that the PETE box can respond to (or interact with) the mist.

At this point there is considerable potential for confusion, some of which you even overhear amongst physicists who get paid to argue about such things. The confusion arises when we are not clear about whether we are considering the mist to be the full and only real state itself, or whether we take it to be just one, amongst many, physical properties. Both options are, in fact, tenable, so let me describe each.

As mentioned, although technically difficult, there is no reason to believe we cannot make a superposition of any given physical properties of a ball. There is nothing special about the color. This suggests the option of just using a mist as the one and only physical property of the ball. In this view the mist is the full real state:

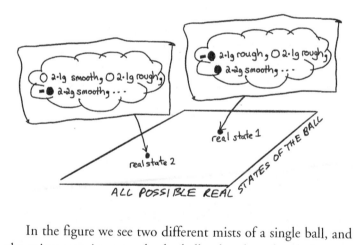

In the figure we see two different mists of a single ball, and the mists contain not only the ball colors but also their mass, perhaps whether their surface is rough or smooth and potentially much more. The details are unimportant for our considerations, but for completeness let me say that that the manner in which a mist is constructed to incorporate multiple different physical properties has many precise rules, and is not quite as arbitrary as the above figure implies. Also I should point out that under this view the real state of more than one ball is just a suitably enlarged mist.

The second option is that we allow for the real states to include the misty state as one of the physical properties, but to potentially include a whole bunch of other things that we do not (yet) know about as well. Under this more conservative view we do not commit to knowing everything about the underlying real states of the world per se. We just say that whatever the real states of the world are, they unambiguously let us (well, the PETE boxes) determine what the misty state is—we can read the misty state off the piece of paper if we know the real state, but perhaps there are other physical properties to read off as well. That is, we use the analogy of the heads-or-tails property of the coin—unarguably real, but just one of a long list of the physical properties. In the case of the coin we divided all the real states into two regions according to whether its real state included heads or tails. For the real states of the ball (whatever they may be) we would need at least four regions like this:

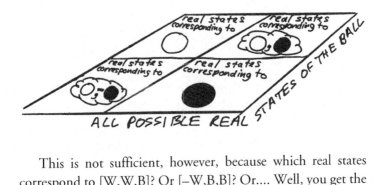

This is not sufficient, however, because which real states correspond to [W,W,B]? Or [–W,B,B]? Or.... Well, you get the picture: we would need to divide the set of real states up into an infinite number of distinct regions, one for each misty state. Note that if you know which point in the plane describes the ball, you know which region it is in, and so you know which misty state describes it.

Both of the options discussed above—one real state per misty state, or many real states per misty state—have the feature that if someone knows the real state of the ball then they also know the misty state. In particular, for both these options there is nothing like the overlap region discussed above for a rocky state. For this reason I will lump them together as options in which we "take the mist as a real physical property," or more simply just that "the mist is real". We just mean that at any point in the set of real states, you can read on the piece of paper uniquely what the appropriate misty state is.

Both options also provide a natural explanation of the two-PETE-boxes conundrum: The ball begins in a real state where it is definitely white; it evolves (via the action of the PETE box) to a real state where it is definitely [W,B]; it then evolves via a second PETE box back to a real state where it is white again; and so on.

Although the details are beyond this book, the main thing to know is that this evolution follows a nice and precise wandering trajectory through the real states (much like the trajectory of a flipped coin through its own series of real states depicted earlier). We can calculate very precisely how one misty state changes into another and that one into yet another as time progresses. In fact this nice type of meandering through the mist occurs for any of the boxes we have encountered, as well as many others we have not. It is all very calm and pleasant.

Until, that is, a human (such as me and I hope you) leaps in and observes the ball.

If misty states are real, should we collapse in confusion?

When we observe the ball, we only ever see it black or white. This means, for example, if the ball is actually in a real state corresponding to a mist such as [W,B], it must immediately "jump" into a different real state for which the ball is definitely black or white, according to what was observed:

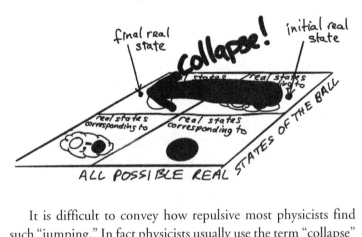

It is difficult to convey how repulsive most physicists find such "jumping." In fact physicists usually use the term "collapse" which sounds more negative. Both words, when they correspond to familiar processes in our everyday lives (such as a building collapsing or a frog jumping), refer to something which is sudden, perhaps very fast, but which is still continuous. By *continuous*, I mean the building's fall or the frog's leap might initially appear to be completely instantaneous, but if you filmed it and then slowed the film right down, you would be able to see all the intermediate stages between the beginning and the end of the jump/collapse process.

We saw a continuous type of evolution through the real states of a coin when I sketched how the real state changes from the time you flip it until the time it lands. If our present laws of physics are correct, however, once you make an observation the misty states necessarily collapse absolutely instantaneously and completely discontinuously. There is no time lag, and there are no intermediate states. The laws essentially demand this for self-consistency, so it is not even a case of us being able to hope that "maybe it just happens so fast we haven't been able to see it in slow-motion yet."

There is no precedent for something like this in even the most sudden physical processes we ever encounter in other areas of our experience—or, for that matter, in all non-misty physics.

To make matters worse, the laws demand that the collapse only ever happens when an observer, such as you or I, looks at the color of the ball. As we considered in Part I, we might employ a wide variety of different techniques to try to observe the ball's color in different ways, some more gentle than others. The collapse process doesn't care about the method we use to interact with the ball, it just happens as soon as that method is strong enough to tell us the ball's color, and it doesn't happen at all otherwise.

Does it then matter in this situation whether or not we actually observe the color? What if we use some kind of unintelligent observing device to probe the ball between the boxes, but we do not look at the color recorded on the device? What we have done is create a really large misty state. The mist representing the ball is now entangled with the mist representing the stuff making up the device. It is this entanglement which causes the "disturbance" to the ball which is responsible for the fact it no longer always falls from the second PETE box the same color it entered the first. However, the actual collapse, the laws claim, only happens when you, the observer, look at this large misty state, either indirectly by reading the device or more directly just looking at the ball. Then the ball mist collapses into "black" or "white" and the observation-device mist collapses into a "black" or "white" reading.

Why should observers be so important? Why should the widely different physical mechanisms they use to interact with the ball make no difference to the final real state the ball ends up in, or how that process occurs?

And if you thought all that was bad enough, consider what happens when we extend our considerations to misty states of two or more balls. Consider the five-ball entangled (generalized Bella) misty state:

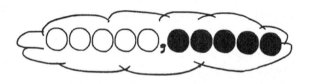

If all misty states are real, then in some large set of all the real states of five balls, there sits this particular state. What happens when we observe one of the balls? At that point we collapse all of the balls to either the state where they are all black, or the state where they are all white—that is, to a completely different real state. None of the balls are left in a misty state, because if one of them is white they all are. That is more disconcerting than the single ball collapse, because the balls in this state can all be in completely different spatial locations.

This means that (again, only if the misty states are real) it is possible in one spatial location to instantaneously change the real state of the world, in another location, arbitrarily far away. Imagine a giant misty state of many balls, spread throughout the universe. Is it really plausible that one person on one little planet orbiting an insignificant star is instantaneously changing the real state of a part of the universe arbitrarily far away?

Faced with all this ugliness surrounding collapse, proponents of the notion that misty states are real have for the most part tried to modify our current physical laws by either (i) trying to find a more physically appealing model of collapse (one where it is proper dynamical process and doesn't need observers); or (ii) trying to find a way to use the misty states as real states, but to completely remove collapse from the picture.

Option (i) is difficult to make compatible with both current and near-future high precision experiments, as well as consistent with other aspects of physical laws (such as not being able to send messages faster than light), which we hold quite dearly. But there are some models which work (at least for the ball type of experiments we have considered; making them work for all experiments we can presently do is more tricky), and which soon will be experimentally ruled in or out.

Option (ii) is more subtle—it typically involves thinking about the absolutely giant misty state that makes up everything in the universe including the observers of the balls, and denying that this giant misty state ever collapses. The challenge then is to extract an explanation of how the very small pieces of that giant mist that comprise you and me experience a world where we can talk about little mists of one and two balls, little mists that give random outcomes when we observe them; a world where the assumption of collapse works so well. (This is often called "the measurement problem.") The most studied option along these lines has been to assume that the giant mist actually describes many different universes, and when you observe the misty state of a single ball there are actually two copies of you created, one that lives in a universe where the ball you observe is white and one where it is black:

Terry Rudolph

It is a dramatically different view of all of physical reality.

A completely different option is to discard the idea that misty states are real, and we now turn to understanding this possibility.

Currency collapse, mental collapse

Imagine you have prepared a coin and flipped it, and you believe that its real state is equally likely to be in the heads region as the tails region of real coin states, as depicted previously. You describe the coin with the appropriate rocky state. Now, before you look at it yourself, a friend you trust tells you "Hey, that coin is heads." At that point you immediately and instantaneously "collapse" your knowledge about the coin. Here is a to-scale diagram of you undergoing mental collapse:

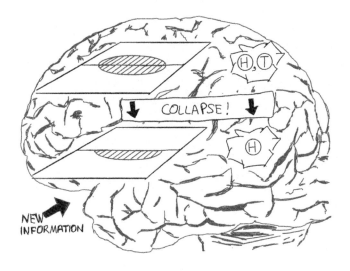

Acquiring information has caused you to change your mind about both the appropriate rocky state and the appropriate distribution over the set of real variables of the coin, because now you know for sure that the coin shows heads.

Such "collapse via updating one's knowledge" is clearly not a physical process as far as the coin is concerned—something changed in your mind, but the coin doesn't care what happens in your mind. It is also clearly something that happens instantaneously; you do not slowly and continuously change the state you assign to the coin. The collapse will occur whenever you gain the appropriate information, and it doesn't matter what physical mechanism you use to acquire that information—if it can provide the requisite information, you collapse; if not, you don't. These are all features shared by the collapse of a misty state, but here they are not at all strange.

These similarities motivate the question: Is it plausible that misty states are also features of our knowledge, rather than real states of the world?

However, there is a very simple dissimilarity between coin collapse and misty state collapse. Collapse of the misty state is accompanied by some tangible disturbance to the experiment, because the output of the second PETE box depends on whether or not you observe the ball after the first PETE box (and cause the collapse).

Because observing the ball involves interacting with it somehow (shining light off it, smelling it, licking it—whatever) it is not ridiculous to conclude: "Collapse happens in my head, which is where misty states live. There is, however, some new fundamental principle of physics which ensures that to probe a system strongly enough to be able to collapse my misty state of knowledge, I must use concrete physical interactions that cause a random disturbance to the real states of that system, whatever they may be." The nice thing about this proposal is that it is completely non-committal about what the "actual real states" of a ball are. I gave in Part I a silly version of such an explanation when I imagined the balls could have hidden stickers on them which PETE boxes manipulate.

However, the proponent of "misty states = real states" counters with: "Why bother thinking about these hidden real states at all? Just let the real state be the misty state and that is the physical thing disturbed by observation."

This in turn stimulates the counterpoint—even if you accept the weird behavior of such a supposedly real physical state when it is disturbed, why can a PETE box see the real states without disturbing them, but we cannot see them at all? What is the principle which decides which devices do or do not cause such disturbance?

Well, comes the rejoinder, *something* enters the top of the second PETE box, since something falls out the bottom, and when we finally observe that something, it always looks like a colored ball. If the physical property of that something is not that it is "really in the misty state" while it is in transit, then why can't you tell me what actually is the real state of that thing about which the mist represents only your knowledge?

Into such back and forth charges no less a person than Albert Einstein, with a brilliant argument (what more do you expect?) that most people understand incompletely. You, I hope, will not be one of them.

Einstein throws himself in completely

Einstein presented an argument to prove that, even if we have no idea what the real states of a ball are, there exist real states in the overlap region of at least two misty states—that is, real states for which there is not a unique corresponding misty state. If a misty state was a physical property of a ball then we would be able to look at the real state and know what the "value of the mist" was (by definition of the real states). Einstein claims to prove there is an overlap between the real states corresponding to two or more misty states, and thus he concludes the "value of the mist" cannot be "on the paper"—it is not a physical property, it is not part of the "real physical state" of a ball.

Einstein's argument is built upon a demonstration that a subjective choice by one person (a.k.a. Alice), arbitrarily far away from a ball held in a storage box by another person (Bob), can collapse Bob's ball to different sets of misty states:

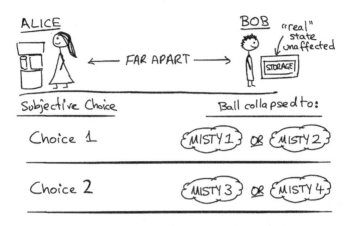

In particular, one of Alice's choices leads Bob's ball to end up in either misty state 1 or 2, while a different choice causes it to end up in either misty state 3 or 4; and all four misty states are different from each other. (Saying they are different means an experiment can be performed for which each misty state predicts a different set of probabilities for concrete observations, not just that they look different as a diagram.)

Alice's measurement, Einstein's argument goes, does not affect Bob's real state. Since she does change the misty states it can be in (at her whim), any given real state must correspond to at least two distinct misty states. More precisely, assuming that (i) a real state of Bob's ball exists, and (ii) the real state of Bob's ball cannot depend on what Alice does arbitrarily far away, Einstein concludes: there are many different misty states corresponding to a single real state of the ball.

For a concrete example, imagine we start with two balls

prepared in the entangled mist [WW,WB,BW] that we encountered in Part II. We give one ball to Alice and one to Bob (Einstein called them A and B; he wasn't a very imaginative guy), who then move far apart from each other.

Alice now chooses between two different experiments to perform. Much like when she was winning your gold, she can choose either to observe her ball directly, or to first pass it through a PETE box before observing it.

In the case where she does nothing first, just observes her ball, she collapses both balls like this:

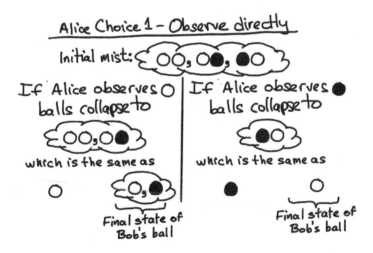

Her other choice is to first pass her ball through a PETE box and then observe it. In doing so she collapses the state of Bob's ball like this:

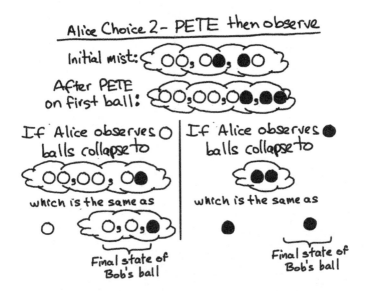

Alice's free choice of measurement—her choice to use the PETE box or not—made far away from Bob, can collapse his ball to either being in one of the states [W,B] or W, or to being in one of the pair of states [W,W,B] or B.

For our particular example Einstein would say that since some of the time Alice collapses Bob's ball to [W,W,B], it must be the case that some of the time the real state of Bob's ball corresponds to [W,W,B], but it must also correspond to one (or both) of either W or [W,B]—the state it would have collapsed to had she done the other measurement. For Einstein's argument it doesn't particularly matter which of these two possibilities [W,W,B] overlaps with.

In terms of our schematic diagrams, Einstein's conclusion that at least some misty states correspond to overlapping sets of real states, perhaps something like this:

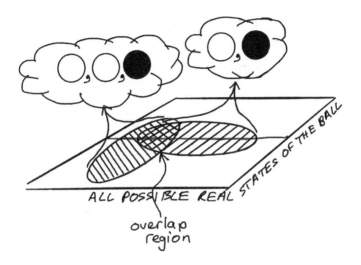

That is enough to prove the misty states are not themselves real.

It is possible to include arbitrarily more misty states in the argument by letting Alice do many more choices of measurements. The final conclusion is that for any given real state of Bob's ball, there are actually arbitrarily many misty states.

Einstein called all this "incompleteness" of the misty state description. He uses the term *incompleteness* (I surmise) because the real state was, by definition, meant to capture all and everything about the physical properties of the ball, and the misty states clearly do not do that if there exist real states in an overlap region of two misty states. But the confusing thing is that we (and he) could also claim the misty states are incomplete if they happened to be just one amongst many physical properties. That is, the "many real states per misty state" option, discussed previously as a more conservative claim about reality of the mist, is also a view in which the misty states are incomplete. Einstein gave other arguments for this very different type of incompleteness, but I'm going to skip them—if I teach you everything there is to know about this topic then you won't be able to make a career as a philosopher, should you so wish, because everything will be clear to you. If you accept the argument of Einstein's just given then whether there are additional underlying physical properties comprising the real states, or whether the mist is the only thing that is real, is moot—the misty states cannot be real at all.

Note in passing that Einstein does not give a sausage (his words) about what Bob does or doesn't measure, or what he can or cannot infer about the properties of his ball. And neither should you—it is irrelevant to this particular argument.

The existence of real states in the overlap region of two misty states would provide a nice explanation of the following: while there is an experiment for which the probabilities of the various outcomes are all different according to whether we drop into it a ball prepared in W or [W,B] or [W,W,B], that experiment never lets determine *for sure* which particular misty state the ball originated in. (This is obvious if we just observe the color, since seeing the ball is white we cannot for sure distinguish the three options, but it actually remains true no matter what experiment we do). If misty states are real, this is somewhat strange—why are we prevented from knowing something that nature knows? However, if we accept Einstein's conclusion, then the reason we cannot always for sure determine whether a ball was prepared in W or [W,B] or [W,W,B] is because sometimes the real state of the ball itself is ambiguous about the matter—that is, in an overlap region compatible with all three of these. By hypothesis, what we mean by the real state is anything and everything that can affect the outcome of an experiment. Thus if the real state itself does not uniquely determine the misty state, neither can any experiment we do. Our inability to distinguish different misty states with certainty is then no more surprising than the fact we cannot always tell for sure, just by seeing a coin with heads facing upwards, whether the person who flipped that coin assigned it the rocky state <H,T> or the rocky state <H,H,T>.

Questioning Einstein's two assumptions

It is natural (and common) to question Einstein's first assumption—the existence of real states. As mentioned at the start of Part III, it would be difficult to question "macroscopic" reality (the stuff we observe directly, and all agree occurs). But we might question the existence of "microscopic reality." This viewpoint calls into question the process whereby we assume (or infer) the existence of microscopic things built from ever-smaller things. In particular, if we question the existence of microscopic reality, we question the assumption that the macroscopic physical properties are built from—or are manifestations of—microscopic ones. The assumption of microscopic reality has served science well, but given the difficulties we have in finding a narrative to explain what the misty states are in terms of well-behaved, microscopic, unobserved real states, perhaps we should abandon the notion that there is any connection between them? (That is, if the real states have meaning or "exist" at all.)

Proponents of this view see the misty states as an inferential tool for predicting the outcomes of future experiments (and how our observations will affect such). In that sense, they propose, the misty states are states of knowledge, but not states of knowledge that tell us anything at all about an underlying reality that is the cause of what we see.

Einstein's second assumption (which he called the "separability hypothesis") was that the real state of Bob's ball cannot depend on what Alice chooses to do with her ball when they are far away from each other. At the time Einstein made his argument, it seemed completely obvious to him (and, in fact, to the people with whom he was arguing) that there could be no question of some kind of mechanical disturbance to (the real state of) Bob's ball based on Alice's measurement choice.

As we now know, based on Part II, "some kind of mechanical disturbance" does have to be contemplated seriously as a possible explanation for the nonlocal correlations. Moreover, it would have to have all of the physically anathematic features that caused Einstein and his contemporaries to dismiss such a thing out of hand. (Einstein's argument preceded the discovery that measurements on entangled misty states can generate nonlocal correlations, as discussed in Part II. Similar to the method the psychics used to get your gold, Einstein's argument requires measurements on an entangled pair of balls. However; he did not discover the type of strong nonlocality presented in Part II, where the data appears in the outcomes of experiments, and does not rely on any interpretation of mathematical objects, mists, or philosophical prejudices.)

With one of Einstein's core assumptions thrown into doubt in such a concrete manner, we cannot rely on his argument to tell us whether every real state of a system uniquely determines a misty state or not. Even worse, in a moment, I will explain an argument built on very, very similar (but arguably less questionable) assumptions than Einstein's; one that reaches the complete opposite conclusion.

Why no faster-than-light communication?

Before we turn to the argument that reaches the opposite conclusion to Einstein's, let me briefly explain why it is that we cannot send messages instantaneously by making measurements on one of an entangled pair of balls. I often hear from people confused about this.

Imagine that Alice, in the experimental setup we've been discussing, wants to communicate something to Bob—let's say either "ATTACK" or "RETREAT." What does she have control over to use as a transmitter? Well, she has one choice: she can observe her ball directly (and collapse Bob's ball to W or [W,B] according to whether she sees her ball is black or white respectively), or she can send it through a PETE box and then observe it (collapsing Bob's ball to B or [W,W,B] according to whether she sees her ball is black or white respectively). Let's say she and Bob have planned that if she observes her ball directly, that means "ATTACK," and if she runs it through the PETE box first, she's sending a "RETREAT" signal.

What does this mean for Bob? A small calculation shows if she observes her ball directly, she will collapse Bob's ball to [W,B] twice as often as to W. That is, the probability of collapsing to [W,B] is 2/3, while the probability of collapsing to W is 1/3. Alternatively, if she wishes to communicate "RETREAT" (and runs her ball through a PETE box first), we find that the probability of collapsing Bob's ball to [W,W,B] is five times as likely as collapsing to B. That is, the probability of collapsing to [W,W,B] is 5/6, while the probability of collapsing to B is 1/6.

The key point is that although Alice can choose which pair to collapse Bob's ball to, she cannot control which member of the pair it ends up in. The probabilities cannot be changed from what the misty states predict.

Bob needs to determine which pair she has collapsed his ball to. Imagine he doesn't do anything to his ball, he just observes its color. When Alice is communicating ATTACK, the probability

Terry Rudolph

he sees a white ball is 1 if she collapsed it to W, and 1/2 if she collapsed it to [W,B]. His overall probability of seeing a white ball is 2/3.

When Alice is communicating RETREAT the probability he sees his ball is white is 0 if she collapsed his ball to B, and 4/5 if she collapsed his ball to [W,W,B] (remember the squaring rule). Since there is a 5/6 chance of collapsing to [W,W,B] the total probability he sees a white ball is the product of 4/5 times 5/6—which is 2/3.

This is identical to his probability if she was communicating the complete opposite message. He has gained no information when he sees his ball is white.

Even if Bob first sends his ball through some complicated array of boxes along with other balls this conclusion remains true. All he sees is that it is equally likely Alice is telling him to attack versus retreat, and so he gains no information at all.

All this is mainly strange if you consider the mist to be real—if you follow Einstein and deny that the real state of Bob's ball is changing at all then you would not expect them to be able to communicate in this manner.

But then how would you explain how the psychics won your gold?

Pooh-Bear creates complete confusion

Any argument contradicting a conclusion of Einstein's should be made by a figure of equivalent stature, although they will, of course, necessarily be of inequivalent intelligence. By consensus of his friends, Winnie-the-Pooh "has no brain." It seems appropriate to attribute these characteristics to an advocate of this counterargument, and so I will call it the Pooh-Bear argument.

Pooh adopts Einstein's first assumption, that there is such a

126

thing as a real state of a ball. Einstein's second assumption was that the real state of Bob's ball cannot depend on what Alice (located arbitrarily far away) does to her ball. The weakness of Einstein's argument, premised as it is on his second assumption, is that it requires the two balls to be entangled. This in turn requires them to, by some means or another, have already come into contact with each other prior to being separated by Alice and Bob. As such they are definitely not necessarily completely independent (entanglement is, in fact, the misty-state manifestation of this). Perhaps when they come into contact they create a magical hole in spacetime that can stretch through extra dimensions and this lets them instantaneously coordinate their actions? Any ridiculous possibility must be considered, and the fact they have had to have some kind of causal connection already to get entangled means it is hard to rule any such things out. The fact the balls have already had this connection also makes the pretty natural expectation that they have real states (physical properties) "all of their own" a lot more questionable.

Pooh replaces Einstein's separability assumption by a separability assumption that is simple enough for even a brainless creature to understand. His assumption is: if two balls have never come into contact (for example, perhaps they were originally created at far corners of the universe), then they have physical properties/real states of their own which are independent from each other, and if you never ever bring the balls together then you can always treat them as separate physical things, completely ignoring the existence of the other one if you like.

Pooh's separability assumption is not a mechanical one like Einstein's. It is an assumption that we can always isolate the things we are examining to a sufficient extent, and treat them as separate physical entities. Without the ability to do independent things we would not actually be able to make scientific progress,

because the process of science is built on "independent verifica-
tion." The thought that we cannot reason and infer things based
on an experiment here, because of what might be going on right
now on the other side of the universe (with which we have not
interacted in billions of years), reaches a new level of absurdity,
and makes one wonder how we could investigate nature at all.
(Although *Nature* has been known to be both absurd and capri-
cious when it comes to such questions.)

Without the ability to consider a rock on Pluto as having its
own properties independent of the properties of a rock here on
Earth, it's very hard to see how we could begin to organize our
thoughts about the world. Never mind tie our shoelaces.

To set the scene for the Pooh-Bear argument, we turn to:

UNIMAGINABLE CONVERSATION
BETWEEN POOH-BEAR AND EINSTEIN

POOH: We should think about what we will have for lunch,
which is always nearby in both time and space thankfully.

EINSTEIN: Time, space? Boring. Although your clock is not
working, which has started me thinking about... hang on a
second, didn't you just have elevenses?!?

POOH: (*Smiling*) Oh yes, I did just have a small something.
Perhaps that is why my Very Little Brain is so ready to
explain. Hey, that rhymes. My "brain" can "explain," hum
tiddely pom...

Pooh begins to hum

EINSTEIN: Ah, Mr. Pooh,...

POOH: Oh sorry, yes, well imagine there are two types of packed lunch. The first type either contains hunny or it contains condensed milk.

EINSTEIN: Honey?

POOH: Yes, hunny. Just one of the two, of course. I wouldn't be allowed to have both. (*Looks wistful, pats his oversize tummy*) I will call that packed lunch the "sweet" option for lunch, because…

EINSTEIN: (*Interrupting*) I think I know why.

POOH: Sorry, I do tend to be a little slow of thought, and perhaps I over-explain. I heard you have a Very Clever Brain. Anyway, the other lunch option contains either hunny or a banana. I'm going to call that the "healthy" option, because…

EINSTEIN: (*Impatiently*) Yes, Mr. Pooh…

POOH: Sorry, there I go again. Now, Christopher Robin is going to pack me either a sweet lunch or a healthy lunch. And Eeyore is, completely independently, going to pack you either a sweet lunch or a healthy lunch, choosing from the same three foods. And then we are going to visit Owl.

EINSTEIN: Good, I have always wished to meet that knowledgeable creature.

POOH: There are four possible lunch combinations we could be carrying: sweet-sweet, sweet-healthy, healthy-sweet and….and….

Pooh looks a bit anxious

EINSTEIN: healthy-healthy?

POOH: (*Smiling*) Yes, exactly, thank you. The plan is to set Owl a challenge. He must tell us, for absolute sure, a lunch combination that was definitely *not* prepared.

EINSTEIN: Why can't he tell us one that *was* prepared?

POOH: I don't really know, this is the only way at the moment that I can make the whole argument work.

EINSTEIN: That is fine. So Owl must definitively rule out one of the four options. I presume he is allowed to look inside the two lunchboxes?

POOH: Oh yes, he can look inside if he wants. Now the question is, will Owl definitely be able to rule out one of the lunch combinations?

EINSTEIN: Well, let's just consider all the possibilities. If Owl sees a banana in my lunchbox and a condensed milk in your lunchbox, he knows the combination prepared was—listing mine first and yours second—definitely "healthy-sweet." So he can say, "The combination prepared was definitely not sweet-sweet." Or, for that matter, he can say it was definitely not healthy-healthy or not sweet-healthy.

POOH: Exactly. In that case there are three different answers he could give, because he knows for sure what was prepared, so he can say for sure what was not prepared.

EINSTEIN: Yes, that's a pretty easy case. The same goes for if he sees bananas in both lunchboxes, or condensed milk in both, or condensed milk in mine and a banana in yours. He knows for sure what was prepared, so he has lots of options to give an answer about what was not prepared.

POOH: What if he sees hunny in your lunchbox and a condensed milk in mine?

EINSTEIN: Hmm. That is more tricky, because honey is both healthy and sweet.

POOH: (*Beaming*) I know, isn't hunny wonderful?

EINSTEIN: So, he knows from the condensed milk in yours that your lunchbox was prepared sweet. But he can't be sure about mine because of the honey.

POOH: Remember the rule was, Owl needs to only tell us one of the combinations that was *not* prepared. He doesn't actually need to know which combination *was* prepared.

EINSTEIN: Aha—I see. Since he knows from the condensed milk that your lunchbox was prepared sweet, he can answer that healthy-healthy was definitely not prepared. Or he can answer that sweet-healthy definitely was not prepared. Because he sees you have the condensed milk, he knows any combination involving your lunchbox being healthy was definitely not prepared.

POOH: Yes, there are only two safe options for him to answer now, but he can still meet the challenge easily.

EINSTEIN: The same will be true whenever one of us has honey and the other one does not. In all those cases Owl will be able to give a satisfactory answer because he will know for sure from the lunchbox without honey how it was prepared.

POOH: You really do think so much faster than me, Mr. Einstein. I have to be honest, that when I was first thinking about this I had to sit and write out all of the options. There were quite a few of them, and I got so absorbed I missed having a little something at eleven o'clock that day. (*Looks sad at the memory*)

EINSTEIN: I can also see now that there is no way that Owl can be certain of winning this challenge. If we played it many times he must eventually be stumped. Because, what can he say if he finds honey in both of our lunchboxes?

POOH: Exactly, Mr. Einstein, you have seen the problem! I think hunny in both lunchboxes would be a Very Good Thing to find, especially if you are willing to share (*glances anxiously at Einstein*). But when that happens Owl will be stumped. He cannot say for sure one of the combinations that was not prepared.

EINSTEIN: I'm not able to see how all this might be relevant to my argument about misty states...

POOH: Well your claim is that just as the two different "states of lunchbox knowledge"—sweet versus healthy—have a "real state" of hunny in common, the misty states have at least some real states in common.

EINSTEIN: Yes, assuming there are such things as real states, and assuming what someone does in one location can't change a real state somewhere far away, it is simple to see that there must be real states common to more than one misty state. I don't know why I've had to spell it out so many times to those...

POOH: Careful Mr. Einstein, children read these books. Well, let's imagine we redo the challenge with Owl, but this time Christopher Robin will prepare me a STORAGE lunchbox that contains one of the infamous black or white balls. And he will either prepare it as a white ball W, or he will prepare it in the misty state [W,B]. Eeyore is independently going to do the same thing for you—prepare you a STORAGE lunchbox that contains a ball either in W or in [W,B]. You should think of W like a "sweet" lunchbox preparation and [W,B] like a "healthy" one.

EINSTEIN: I see. My claim is that W and [W,B] are not themselves the real states because by my argument there are at least some real states common to both of them. Those common real states are like the honey. Even if Owl is so wise and knowledgeable that he can see real states, whatever they may be, at least some of the time both balls will be in a honey-like real state. This makes it impossible for Owl to always say one combination that was *not* prepared.

POOH: Yes, yes—now we are there. Because here is the amazing thing. Owl always manages to win this challenge!

EINSTEIN: What? Are you sure?

POOH: Yes, we did it many, many times. In fact it doesn't matter which pair of misty states Christopher Robin and

Eeyore pick from, Owl can always meet the challenge. This is why I claim that every real state is associated with one and only one misty state.

EINSTEIN: Remarkable. Things are really not the Things that they seem to be.

POOH: Oh I am so glad you appreciate that. When you are a Bear of Very Little Brain, and you Think of Things, you find sometimes that a Thing which seemed very Thingish inside you is quite different when it gets out into the open and has other people looking at it.

How can Owl do it?

Owl needs to take the two balls from Pooh and Einstein—about which he only knows that they could be in any one of the four misty states WW, W[W,B], [W,B]W, or [W,B][W,B]—and rule out one of the four combinations.

The schematic of the procedure Owl devised (with a little help from Rabbit, Tigger and Roo) is to take Pooh's and Einstein's balls (without looking at them) and drop them through these boxes:

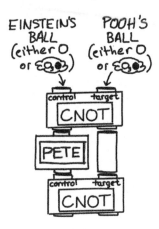

Working out what happens for the four different possible input misty states is old hat to you by now:

Holding Einstein's ball in storage, the next stage of Owl's procedure is to look at the color of Pooh's ball. If he observes Pooh's ball is black he then observes Einstein's ball directly, but if he sees it is white he first drops Einstein's ball through a PETE box and then observes it.

Ball 2 is black: If Owl sees Pooh's ball is black, then he releases Einstein's ball from storage and directly observes it. Looking at the four possible output mists in the above figure, we see that the only configurations appearing which have Pooh's ball black are BB and WB. We further note that the WB configuration could have resulted from three of the possible combinations that Einstein and Pooh might have presented Owl with. It does not, however, appear in the output mist when both Pooh's and Einstein's balls started out white (top left corner figure). So, if Owl sees that Pooh's ball is black and then sees that Einstein's ball is white, he can safely announce "it is not the case that both balls were initially prepared white."

Similarly, the BB configuration does not appear in the output mist when the two balls Owl drops in are [W,B][W,B] (bottom right corner figure). Therefore if he sees both balls are black he announces "it is not the case that both balls were initially prepared in the misty state [W,B]."

Ball 2 is white: If Owl sees Pooh's ball is white after the CNOT-PETE-CNOT series, he collapses the two balls according to these rules:

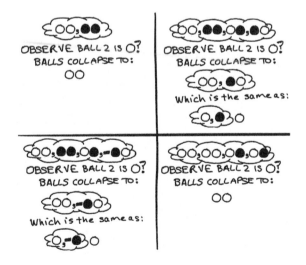

Let's say the balls were W[W,B] at the very start, when Eeyore and Christopher Robin separately packed them. After passing the three boxes this has evolved to the situation in the top right corner figure of this diagram. Therefore, Owl seeing Pooh's ball is white means Einstein's ball is now in the misty state [W,B]. If Owl now passes Einstein's ball through a PETE box, he will definitely observe it to be white.

If, on the other hand, the balls were [W,B]W at the very start (bottom left corner figure), then, after Owl observes Pooh's ball is white, Einstein's ball is in the misty state [W,−B]. If Owl now passes Einstein's ball through a PETE box, he will definitely observe it to be black.

Thus, if Owl sees Einstein's ball is black he safely announces "it is not the case that Einstein's ball was initially W and Pooh's ball initially [W,B]." If he sees Einstein's ball is white he announces "it is not the case that Einstein's ball was initially [W,B] and Pooh's ball initially W."

This is quite a complicated procedure to verify works (and after all that, Pooh and Einstein have to go back to Eeyore and Christopher Robin to check if Owl was right). It has the feature that Owl does not even have to look at the mysterious, apparently invisible real state of the balls, he just passes them through some simple boxes and observes their color. We don't know what goes on inside the boxes—perhaps they can look at real physical states, but Owl does not need to (although he probably would claim that he can).

Recapping, rexplaining

The basic question we are addressing is: although we have no clue what the underlying real physical properties of a ball in a misty state might be, can we deduce something about the relationship between misty states and the presumed real states? Einstein gave an argument that the relationship must be "many-to-one," that is, there are many different misty states corresponding to a single real state. His method was to show that one person's arbitrary choice in handling a ball in their possession can cause a remote ball (arbitrarily far away from the first one) to end up in one of many different misty states. Assuming distant subjective choices should not change what is "really going on" with a ball, his conclusion follows. Einstein's argument requires the two balls in question initially be entangled, it makes a strong presumption of locality and (in light of the nonlocal correlations generated by measurements on entangled states discussed in Part II) it can be considered suspect.

As with Einstein, Pooh's goal is deduce something about the relationship between misty states and real states of a single ball. Pooh-Bear's argument also used two balls. For both Einstein's and Pooh's arguments two balls are necessary because it is known that observations on just a single ball cannot be used to distinguish between the possibilities of whether the misty states overlap on the real states (whatever they may be) or not.

Pooh's argument explicitly relied on the balls not being initially entangled; in fact, it relies on them having been prepared independently (by Christopher Robin and Eeyore), and this assumption of preparation independence replaces Einstein's "obvious" locality assumption that an arbitrarily distant choice in handling one ball cannot change the real state of another ball.

Before his argument dealing with two balls Pooh first considered the example of a single lunchbox that can be prepared in two different ways, "sweet" or "healthy," such that there is a real state (honey) common to both possible preparations. If you happen to open a single lunchbox like this and see honey, there is no way to tell which of the two preparations was used. A similar situation arises with balls in misty states—in general two different misty states of a single ball cannot be distinguished with certainty. But with the balls, unlike the lunchboxes, we cannot see the proposed real states. As such it is unclear if the inability to distinguish them is because there are overlapping real states, that is, real states in common to both, just as Einstein argued there must be. Alternatively, it could just have to do with some fundamental restriction on the kinds of boxes we can build and observations we can make.

What Pooh argued was that the presence of honey—a real state in common to both possible preparations of a single lunchbox—also made impossible a different type of game you can play with two lunchboxes. This is the slightly strange game where Owl has to say which of the four possible combinations of two lunchboxes was not prepared.

Putting balls inside the lunchboxes using different preparations of misty states is a game changer (and less palatable). Unlike the case of preparation of sweet versus healthy lunches, if a ball is placed in each lunchbox prepared in one of two different misty states, then there does exist a way for Owl to win the game. This was shown explicitly for the case where the ball was prepared either W or [W,B], but something similar can be done for any pair of possible misty state preparations.

Pooh's conclusion is that there cannot be real states compatible with two different misty states, so that there are completely distinct regions of real states for any misty state, much like this diagram from earlier:

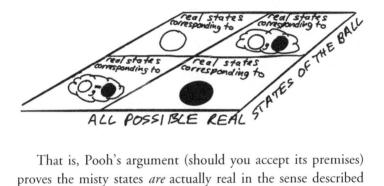

That is, Pooh's argument (should you accept its premises) proves the misty states *are* actually real in the sense described near the beginning of this part of the book.

Final thoughts

There are a many, many arguments that I have not covered, both for and against thinking of the mist as real. I have tried to explain, and get you interested in, the challenges on both sides—not to indoctrinate you with my own ever-fungible opinions.

I personally live in cognitive dissonance: on a day-to-day basis I talk about the physical properties of the photons (from which I am currently trying to build the mystical computer discussed in Part I) as if they are as tangible as any of the physical properties of the human-scale objects in the room around me. They are not. I suspect I should treat the misty states as states of knowledge, but to be understood within a more general framework of theories of inference than our present theories find comfortable.

The extreme view along these lines is to say we can only use the misty states to infer about potential happenings within the world that we may, by our personal choices, bring to being with our observations. That we should not attempt to connect those happenings to... well to stuff actually going on. While this extreme view may seem strange to us now, there was a time that the gods were attributed responsibility for the events of the world. Thousands of years ago the radical view (best captured by Lucretius in *De Rerum Natura*) was to propose that actually the things important to humans were just flotsam of the motion of microscopic constituents. This perspective eventually won out, and has served science incredibly well—it is difficult (for me) to let go of.

But because all attempts to provide an underpinning narrative for what is "really going on" when we do experiments in the mist—nonlocality being my personal bugbear—I have no confidence in the "correctness" of any of the physical properties our theories are premised upon. It seems crazy that I should either abandon the idea there is stuff doing things out there that doesn't care about me, or believe my experiences of the world can depend on things happening in a galaxy far, far away.

In the end I guess I cannot escape my naive realistic belief that there is stuff there, and it has physical properties of some form independent of my concerns. I am willing to contemplate the possibility that perhaps all the physical properties I implicitly consider fundamental are merely artifacts of the evolution of human perceptions, their presumed importance an anthropocentric mistake. Confronted by nonlocal correlations, I sometimes even wonder if space and time—important properties for monkeys who need to find food and mates—might be no more relevant to the true underlying reality of the universe than the pleasant smell of a banana.

Summary of Part III

* Although we have only discussed the color of a ball as a property, any physical property can be "put into" a misty state.

* The relationship of the mathematical object of a misty state to "real physical properties" is contentious.

* One option is to take the mist itself as a real physical property. This results either in some weird mechanical properties of the mist (if we accept collapse) or problems to do with explaining our own experiences within a single universe.

* Another option is to take the mist as a state of knowledge. Within this option there are two possibilities. The misty states might be states of knowledge (like rocky states) where the macroscopic-scale events they represent arise from underlying real states. Or the misty states (not at all like rocky states) might be a new type of inferential object, which does not need a connection to underlying "real states."

* If there are real underlying states (i.e. properties) of physical objects, then, Einstein argued, there are multiple misty states corresponding to a single real state. His argument assumed locality. This assumption is particularly questionable as he also needed entangled states, which we now know can produce nonlocal correlations.

* Without using entangled misty states, but also with a different locality/independence assumption, Pooh-Bear gave an argument for the opposite conclusion to Einstein— namely that real states correspond to unique misty states.

Epilogue

Quantum. It is a word I read hundreds of times a week in scientific papers. But here I was in an airport pharmacy, buying underarm deodorant, reading that magical word through the mental fog of travel fatigue. My armpits definitely need to be "quantum dry," so I purchased it. I long ago gave up being irritated by stupid use of the q-word in everything from "quantum auto-body repair" to "quantum financial services." As a word that actually originated in describing the very smallest quantities of stuff, calling your product a "quantum leap" makes about as much sense as advertising it as "miniscule progress you definitely won't notice but which you should pay more for."

Although this has been a book about quantum theory—the most important theory of modern physics—I have avoided using the word "quantum" per se. Primarily this is because I want to avoid what is now extremely loaded jargon about which a ridiculous number of misconceptions abound. Many of these misconceptions are due to poor use of language describing much more precise mathematics and/or experimental facts. My goal here has been to teach those facts and avoid the jargon. There is also the danger of thinking that quantum theory is difficult to sort out because we cannot "see" the microscopic things to which we normally apply it. But in fact you can see with your naked eye the fluorescence from a single atom.

We could therefore build boxes very much as I have presented, where instead of black and white balls we would see something like a small dot of red or green light bouncing off (or emitted by) an atom. We have no indications whatsoever (and in fact many to the contrary) that quantum theory will fail to be the correct description of the world up to human scales. The difficulty of building PETE boxes for large-scale objects appears to be only one of engineering. If somehow quantum theory fails to be the correct theory at larger scales that would be a remarkable discovery.

The "misty states" are just "quantum states," and the phenomena of nonlocality and entanglement and superposition would often be called "quantum nonlocality" and "quantum entanglement," and "quantum superposition." I have taken "the laws of quantum physics" to be the axioms of the theory as typically taught to an undergraduate physicist (often associated with what is called a "Copenhagen Interpretation" although they are basically just the rules taken at face value, and not really an interpretation of those rules per se).

As Part I hopefully convinced you, we are entering an age of amazing new technologies based on these counterintuitive phenomena. Actually there are many things we already use every day that rely on quantum phenomena. The internet is powered by lasers, which require quantum physics. The GPS system relies on atomic clocks, which require quantum physics. Although remarkable and important, these, and many other, "old quantum technologies" are basically only making use of "quantum superposition"— the phenomenon which can be exhibited by a single ball in a misty state of black and white. The challenge is to build larger, entangled, misty states with which we can do even more valuable things. It is a challenge I am having fun taking on, and perhaps you can join in one day too.

It is also fun to try and come up with "natural" explanations of quantum weirdness, but hopefully you now realize that this is an extremely challenging task, and should be approached with both care and precision.

History, Context and Further Reading

I intend to put some material on www.qisforquantum.org, both to help understand misty states better, as well as to try and connect the formalism of the mist to regular quantum theory for students who go on to university level study.

Although the misty balls do not easily describe every possible part of quantum theory, they are an extremely powerful subset, universal for quantum computing, and so in principle can simulate and calculate everything in the full theory. This means there are many other parts of quantum theory I did not try to cover that can be readily learned in this diagrammatic form—the uncertainty principle, teleportation, secret key distribution, all the main quantum algorithms, superdense coding and so on.

Part I

Let me relate some other jargon, which you will hear as you go about your physics reading, to things you now know from this book. "Wave-particle duality" is just one manifestation of the phenomenon that a ball can sometimes be "definitely white" and sometimes "definitely in a misty state of black and white." A ball that is definitely black or white is like a particle. A ball in a misty state is "wavy" because, just as a peak in a water wave can

Terry Rudolph

interfere with a trough to yield no wave at all, a ball configuration with a negative-sign label can cancel with one with a positive sign label. The Wikipedia articles *Wave–particle_duality* and *Interference_(wave_propagation)* are a good start if you want to understand a bit more. However, once we are considering two or more balls, there are very many other ways in which misty states are not at all like water waves (or any other regular physical waves), so the usefulness of this wave/particle way of thinking is debatable.

"Quantum coherent" means (in the terms we've been using) "misty"; "relative phase" or "quantum phase" refers to the negative-sign labels. The weirdness of quantum superposition is often prosaically illustrated in terms of Schroedinger's cat being in a (misty state) superposition of dead and alive. Schroedinger actually used the cat to illustrate the even weirder phenomenon of quantum entanglement, discussed in Part II.

The remarkable (to me) fact that I can go so far in building up proper quantum theory for you using only basic arithmetic is due to the proof by Shih (arxiv.org/abs/quant-ph/0205115) that the Toffoli plus Hadamard gates are universal for quantum computing, which means in fact they could be used to accurately calculate any quantum phenomena. The Toffoli gate is just our CCNOT box, the Hadamard gate is the infamous PETE box. (The infamous Pete person is at peteshadbolt.co.uk). The CSWAP box can be used in place of the CCNOT, and its universality for regular computation was discovered by Fredkin. The Wikipedia articles *Toffoli_gate*, *Quantum_gate#Hadamard_gate* and *Fredkin_gate* have more information.

If you are interested in the interplay between our processes of logical reasoning and computation, then it is worth reading the introduction to Turing's famous papers which formalized them, along with one of Andrew Hodges' many books or essays about

Turing at www.turing.org.uk/publications/. If you want to go the next step to understanding more quantum information theory try Scott Aaronson's Quantum Computing Since Democritus (www.scottaaronson.com/democritus/).

The robbing-a-bank example I used to illustrate the power of multi-ball misty state (quantum) computation is called the Deutsch-Jozsa algorithm; I stole the idea of using a bank robbery to explain this algorithm from Naomi Nickerson.

Part II

The remarkable discovery that quantum theory allows for the generation of nonlocal correlations is due to Bell, and is typically called Bell's Theorem. Coincidentally, his version makes use of the "Bella" misty state. The particular game with the psychics that I set up exhibits a special case of a version of quantum nonlocality due to Hardy (doi.org/10.1103/PhysRevLett.71.1665). Hardy's paper is difficult to understand; I provide the link for completeness only. The Wikipedia article on Bell's theorem isn't great at the time of writing, and the internet is full of incomprehensible, wrong, or overly technical stuff about quantum nonlocality. Good luck. However Bell's original papers, some of which are not overly technical, are still a beautiful read. They are collected in the book *Speakable and Unspeakable in Quantum Mechanics*.

It is more common when discussing nonlocal quantum correlations to consider a game due to Clauser, Horne, Shimony, and Holt that the psychics win if they give the same color answers (BB or WW) if either one, or both, of them are told tails, and opposite color answers (BW or WB) when both are told tails. There are no other rules per se. Any local strategy can only win this game 75% of the time (known as the CHSH inequality), but with the psychics sharing balls prepared in the Bella mist it can be won over 85% of the time. I may add a fuller discussion to the webpage for the book if enough people are interested in it.

I have only touched on the options people consider seriously for avoiding unpleasant consequences or conclusions of nonlocal correlations. An option that treats the mist as a physically real medium (with all the requisite weird properties necessary) is Bohm-de Broglie theory, Wikipedia has a decent exposition at *De_Broglie–Bohm_theory*.

If you start reading around this area there is a lot of confusion. For instance, people often conflate or equate the Einstein-Podolsky-Rosen paradox with Bell's theorem. EPR's paradox is about incompleteness, addressed in Part III, but it is more poorly explained than Einstein did on his own in other places. In fact all aspects of the EPR paradox can be reproduced in a local theory (as pointed out originally by Bell) and so it is distinct from Bell's considerations. Because the EPR paper itself mashed up incompleteness with Heisenberg's uncertainty principle, in Part III, I have chosen to use the much clearer argument for incompleteness Einstein gave in a letter (EA 47-22 at the Einstein archives) to Schroedinger.

Part III

More precise distinctions between types of explanations for the quantum state are elucidated by Harrigan and Spekkens at arxiv.org/abs/0706.2661. To read more on models with dynamical collapse, find the Stanford Encyclopedia of Philosophy's (plato.stanford.edu) article *qm-collapse*. To read more on many-universe (non-collapse) explanations try their article *qm-manyworlds* or Wallace's book, *The Emergent Multiverse*. The multiverse/many-worlds view is an example of taking the mist to be real, and taking it to be the only real state (the "first option" discussed in the text). An example where the mist is taken as real but there are other physical properties in the real states as well (the "second option") is Bohm-de Broglie theory mentioned above.

If you want to read excerpts from the letter EA 47-22 to Schroedinger where Einstein made his argument most clearly (along with some musings on how Einstein or Schroedinger could have discovered Bell's theorem) then try arxiv.org/abs/1411.4387. Gilder's lovely book *The Age of Entanglement* seems to get the conceptual history mostly right, as do any of the papers by Howard (www3.nd.edu/~dhoward1/) upon which it is partly based.

Einstein also sometimes gave an argument along the lines that since a misty state of [W,B] sometimes looks like the "observably real" state W and sometimes like the "observably real" state B when we look at the ball, there is clearly more than one real state for a misty (i.e. quantum) state. This is an argument for the "second option" for taking the mist to be real, discussed in the text, namely that many different real states corresponding to a single misty state. It is a different form of "incompleteness", and confusion with Bell's theorem and the EPR paradox and Einstein's letter to Schroedinger is rife.

Such a type of incompleteness would not alleviate us from all the "unphysical" properties of the real states when we take the mist to be real, for example that a measurement on one ball of the mist [WWWW,BBBB] in one location can change the purported real state of the world at arbitrarily distant locations. In the text I have focused on the stronger argument Einstein gave as to why misty and real states were not in "one to one correspondence", because it is very often misunderstood, and, for reasons discussed in the Harrigan and Spekkens paper mentioned above, would have been much stronger in terms of ruling out various "realist interpretations" of quantum theory, had it not been found suspect by Bell's discovery of nonlocality. Reading any of the writings of Fine, such as *The Shaky Game*, is a way of getting into this somewhat confusing topic.

In modern papers you will often read about "ontic states" (what I called real states) and the distinction between "the mist (quantum state) is real" versus "the mist (quantum state) is just knowledge/information about the real state" referred to as "psi-ontic" and "psi-epistemic" respectively.

Approaches to (and arguments for) understanding quantum states as epistemic can be found in Ballentine's textbook *Quantum Mechanics: A Modern Development*, in Spekkens' classic paper arxiv.org/abs/quant-ph/0401052, in Brukner and Zeilinger's discussion arxiv.org/abs/quant-ph/0212084, and in any of the many papers on QBism by Fuchs and collaborators, for example arxiv.org/abs/1412.4211. QBism is an example of an approach that denies a connection between real states/physical properties and how we use the mist to explain our experiences and interactions with the world. There are also many great links and references in the article *qt-issues* at the Stanford Encyclopedia of Philosophy.

The "Pooh-Bear" argument is from arxiv.org/abs/1111.3328, but Leifer's blog post *can-the-quantum-state-be-interpreted-statistically* is a good place to start if you want a clearer explanation. The very last sentence Pooh says to Einstein is direct quotation from *Winnie-the-Pooh* by A. A. Milne. The rest I made up.

Acknowledgements

My deep appreciation to Andrew Simmons, Naomi Nickerson and Jan Hazla for so many useful comments on very rough drafts, to Louisa Gilder for excellent, thoughtful micro- and macro-scopic editing, to Nic Harrigan for both technical help and encouragement (well, badgering) to engage in science communication and Ivan and Brenda Rudolph for proof-reading, great discussions, and life, all of which helped greatly in making this book possible.